First Edition

S0-ASH-204

triumphlearning™
Common Core Coach
Mathematics 2

Dr. Jerry Kaplan
Senior Mathematics Consultant

Common Core Coach, Mathematics, First Edition, Grade 2   T213NA   ISBN-13: 978-1-61997-999-4
Cover Illustration: Daron Parton/Deborah Wolfe Ltd.

Triumph Learning® 136 Madison Avenue, 7th Floor, New York, NY 10016

Contents

Common Core
State Standards

 Problem Solving   Fluency Lesson   Performance Task

Domain 1
Operations and Algebraic Thinking

Domain 1
Operations and Algebraic Thinking

Tomatoes

Cabbage

Peppers

Eggplant

Zucchini

Corn

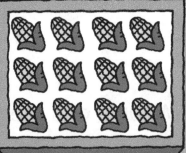

How many more tomatoes than peppers are in the garden?

★ You can **add** to solve word problems.
The numbers you add are **addends**.
The answer is the **sum**.

Draw groups and put them together to find how many in all.

Example 1

Melanie has 7 marbles.

Diego has 12 marbles.

How many marbles do Melanie and Diego have in all?

$7 + 12 = \rule{1cm}{0.4cm}$

Melanie's marbles   Diego's marbles   marbles in all

7   +   12   =

▶ Melanie and Diego have _____ marbles in all.

★ Write an **equation** to solve an addition word problem. Use a symbol, such as ■ or ▲, to stand for a missing number.

Example 2

Yuri has 35 buttons.

Ann gives him a bag with 30 more buttons.

How many buttons does Yuri have now?

$35 + 30 = $ ■

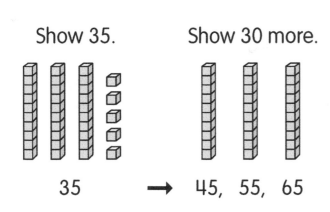

Show 35.   Show 30 more.

35 → 45, 55, 65

$35 + 30 = \boxed{65}$

▶ Yuri now has _____ buttons.

Example 3

Zoey and Kevin collect coins.

Zoey has 40 more coins than Kevin has.

Kevin has 38 coins.

How many coins does Zoey have?

Zoey has **40 more** coins than Kevin.
So **add 40** to Kevin's number to find Zoey's number.

Write and solve an equation.

Kevin's number	plus	40	equals	Zoey's number
↓	↓	↓	↓	↓
38	+	40	=	■

$40 = 10 + 10 + 10 + 10$

Add 10 to make 40.

$38 + 10 = 48$

$48 + 10 = 58$

$58 + 10 = 68$

$68 + 10 = 78$

So $38 + 40 = \boxed{78}$.

▶ Zoey has _____ coins.

★ Use a drawing to show that two addends are joined together to make the sum.

Example 4

Kayla has some stamps.

Liam has 63 stamps.

Kayla and Liam have 83 stamps in all.

How many stamps does Kayla have?

▨ + 63 = 83

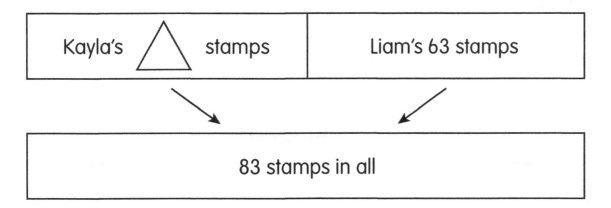

Start with the addend you know: Liam's 63 stamps

Add 10. $63 + 10 = 73$

Add 10 more. $73 + 10 = 83$

So $63 + 20 = 83$.

| 20 | + 63 = 83

▶ Kayla has _____ stamps.

★ Sometimes word problems have more than one step.

Example 5

Austin had 12 blue blocks and 3 red blocks.

His dad gave him some more blocks.

Now Austin has 45 blocks.

How many blocks did Austin's dad give him?

1

Find how many blocks Austin had at the start.

$12 + 3 = $ ▮

Count on 3: $12 \rightarrow 13, 14, 15$

So $12 + 3 = \boxed{15}$.

Austin had 15 blocks at the start.

2

Find how many blocks Austin's dad gave him.

$15 + \triangle = 45$

Add 10. $15 + 10 = 25$

Add 10 more. $25 + 10 = 35$

Add 10 more. $35 + 10 = 45$

So $15 + \triangle{30} = 45$

▶ Austin's dad gave him _____ blocks.

Maya has 27 puzzle pieces.

Jason has 50 more puzzle pieces than Maya.

How many puzzle pieces does Jason have?

$27 + 50 = $ ▢

Use models to show the puzzle pieces.

Maya's 27 pieces   50 more

Count on to add.

50 more

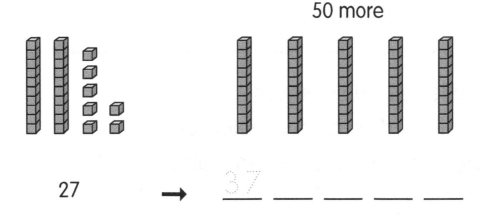

27   →   37 ___ ___ ___ ___

$27 + 50 = $ ▢

▶ Jason has _____ puzzle pieces.

1 Ruby had some toys. She got 20 more toys.
Now she has 54 toys in all. How many toys did
Ruby have to start?

$$\boxed{} + 20 = 54$$

---

2 Kent plays the organ for 45 minutes.
He has lunch and plays for 30 more minutes.
How long does Kent play the organ?

$$45 + 30 = \boxed{}$$

---

3 Lily collected 39 seashells.
Sue collected some seashells, too.
In all, they collected 89 seashells.
How many seashells did Sue collect?

$$39 + \boxed{} = 89$$

4 Serge had 24 model cars and 8 model trucks. His uncle gives him 20 more model cars and trucks. How many model cars and trucks in all does Serge have now?

$24 + 8 = \boxed{32}$

$\square + 20 = \triangle$

5 **SOLVE** Lauren had 22 stamps. She bought 30 more stamps. Then her friend gave her 6 stamps. How many stamps does Lauren have in all?

Write equations and solve the problem. Show your work.

★ You can **subtract** to solve word problems.
When you subtract one number from another,
the answer is the **difference**.

Example 1

There are 19 smiley stickers.

Of these, 8 are blue. The rest are yellow.

How many stickers are yellow?

$19 - 8 = $

Draw the whole group.

Draw 19 smiley stickers.

Make 8 smiley stickers blue.

Make the rest of the stickers yellow.

Count the smiley stickers that are yellow.

$19 - 8 = \boxed{}$

▶ There are _____ yellow stickers.

Example 2

A squirrel had 20 acorns.

It ate 5 of them.

How many acorns were left?

$20 - 5 = $ ▨

Draw the whole group. Draw 20 acorns.

Take 5 acorns from the group.

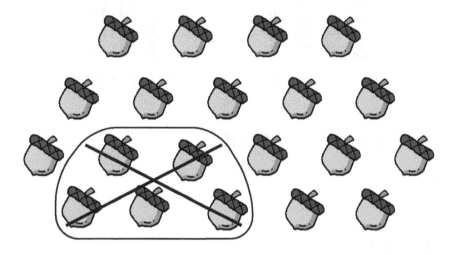

Find the number of acorns that are left.

$20 - 5 = \boxed{15}$

▶ There were _____ acorns left.

Example 3

Blake had 70 pennies.

He spent some pennies.

Then he had 30 pennies left.

How many pennies did Blake spend?

70 − ▨ = 30

Show 70 in all.

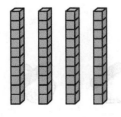 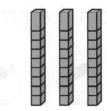

pennies spent   30 were left.

4 tens show the pennies spent.

4 tens = 40

70 − $\boxed{40}$ = 30

▶ Blake spent _____ pennies.

Example 4

Some walnuts were on the table.

Sharon ate 10 walnuts.

Then 24 walnuts were left.

How many walnuts were on the table to start?

▲ − 10 = 24

Use a drawing.

One addend is 10.

The other addend is 24.

The sum is the number of walnuts at the start.

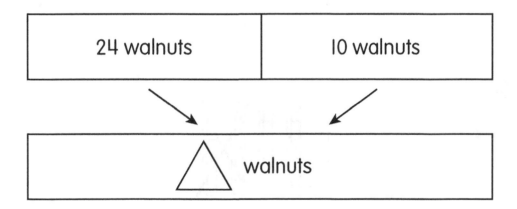

The missing number is the sum. Add the addends to find the sum.

24 + 10 = 34

△34 − 10 = 24

▶ There were _____ walnuts on the table to start.

Example 5

Luke has 20 fewer games than Mary-Jo.

Mary-Jo has 50 games.

How many games does Luke have?

Luke has **20 fewer** games than Mary-Jo.
So **subtract 20** from Mary-Jo's number to
find Luke's number.

Write and solve an equation.

Mary-Jo's number	minus	20	equals	Luke's number
↓	↓	↓	↓	↓
50	−	20	=	▪

Show 50.
Subtract 20.

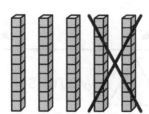

There are 3 tens left.

3 tens = 30

So 50 − 20 = ___30___.

▶ Luke has _____ games.

★ Sometimes word problems have more than one step.

Example 6

Haley had 18 storybooks and 3 animal books.
Then she gave away some books. Now she has
19 books in all. How many books did she give away?

①

Find how many books Haley had at the start.

$18 + 3 = \blacksquare$

Count on 3: $18 \rightarrow 19, 20, 21$

So $18 + 3 = \boxed{21}$.

Haley had 21 books at the start.

②

Find how many books Haley gave away.

$21 - \blacktriangle = 19$

Write a related addition sentence.

$19 + \blacktriangle = 21$

Count from 19. Find how many you add to make 21.

$19 \rightarrow 20, 21 \qquad 19 + 2 = 21$

So $21 - \triangle\!\!2 = 19$.

▶ Haley gave away _____ books.

Lucy has 30 fewer coins than Gavin.

Gavin has 80 coins.

How many coins does Lucy have?

$80 - 30 =$ ▢

Use models to show Gavin's coins.

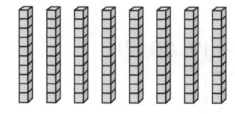

Show that Lucy has fewer coins than Gavin.
Cross out 30.

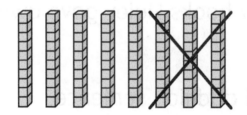

There are 5 tens left.

5 tens = 50

$80 - 30 =$ $\boxed{50}$

▶ Lucy has _____ coins.

Practice

1 Madison had 96 action figures.
She gave some to her friend Tommy.
Now she has 56 action figures.
How many action figures
did Madison give to Tommy?

$$96 - \boxed{} = 56$$

2 Evan had some toys in the attic.
He took 20 of them down from the attic.
Now there are 33 toys in the attic.
How many toys were in the attic before?

$$\boxed{} - 20 = 33$$

3 Luis wants to practice his trumpet
for 75 minutes. He practiced for 60 minutes.
Then he stopped to talk on the phone.
For how many more minutes will Luis practice?

$$75 - 60 = \boxed{}$$

4 Taylor's class is making designs for a school art contest. The girls made 27 designs. The boys made 30 designs. The teacher chose 20 of the designs to enter in the contest. How many of the designs were not entered in the contest?

$$27 + 30 = \boxed{}$$

$$\boxed{} - 20 = \triangle$$

5 **SOLVE** Alex had 72 marbles. He sold 30 of his marbles. Then his friend gave him 6 marbles. How many marbles does Alex have in all?

Write equations and solve the problem. Show your work.

⭐ One way to add is to count on.

Example 1

3 + 7 = ▨

1. Start with the greater number.
   Show 7 blocks.

2. Add 3 more blocks.

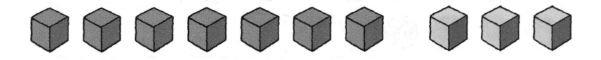

3. Count on from the greater number.
   Start with 7. Count on 3.

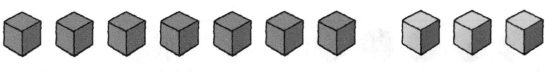

   7 → 8 9 10

▶ 3 + 7 = ☐

★ You can make a ten to add.

Example 2

$9 + 4 = $ □

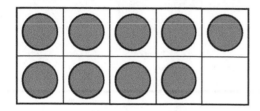   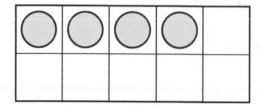

1

Make a ten. Start with 9.

Move 1 yellow counter to fill that ten-frame.

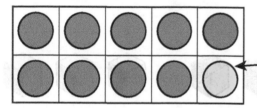   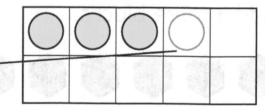

$9 + 4$ is the same amount as $10 + 3$.

2

Count on to find the sum.

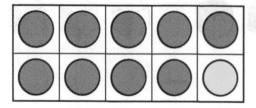   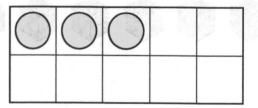

10   →   11   12   <u>13</u>

▶ $9 + 4 = $ □

Think about ten when you subtract.

Example 3

$16 - 9 =$ ▢

Show 16. Subtract to get a difference of 10.

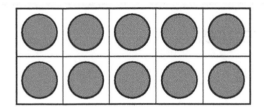

$16 - 6 = 10$

 Think of 9 as 6 and another number.

$9 = 6 + 3$

 Subtract 3 more.

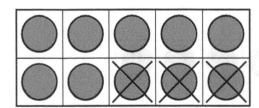 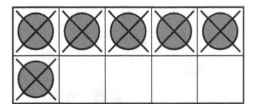

$16 - 6 = 10$

$10 - 3 = \underline{7}$

▶ $16 - 9 =$ ▢

★ **Use related facts to subtract.**

Example 4

$$\begin{array}{r} 14 \\ -\ 8 \\ \hline \end{array}$$

1

Write a related addition sentence.

8 plus what number equals 14?

8 + ▢ = 14

2

Start with 8 yellow counters.

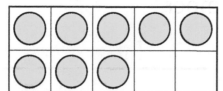

3

Use red counters to make 14.

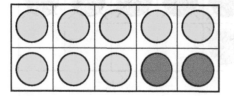 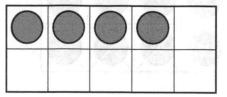

8 + ___6___ = 14

▶
$$\begin{array}{r} 14 \\ -\ 8 \\ \hline \ \square\ \end{array}$$

Use doubles and doubles-plus-1 to add.

Example 5

$7 + 8 = \boxed{}$

1

Think about doubles.

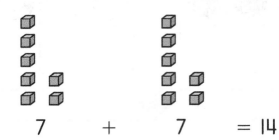

$$7 \quad + \quad 7 \quad = 14$$

2

Think about doubles-plus-1.

7 + 8 is 1 more than 7 + 7.

7 + 8 is the same amount as 7 + 7 + 1.

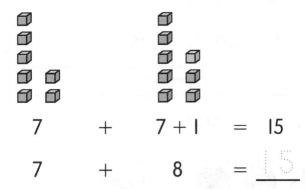

$$7 \quad + \quad 7 + 1 \quad = \quad 15$$

$$7 \quad + \quad 8 \quad = \quad \underline{15}$$

▶ $7 + 8 = \boxed{}$

8 + 4 = ▢

Show 8 counters.   Show 4 counters.

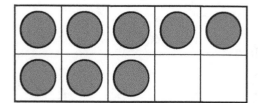   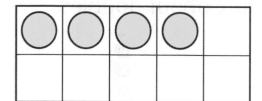

2

Make a ten. Start with ___8___.

Move yellow counters to fill a ten-frame.

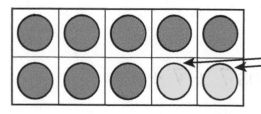   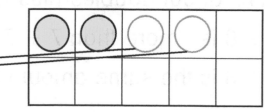

8 + 4 is the same amount as _____ + _____.

3

Count on to find the sum.

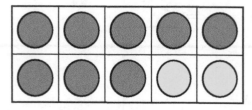   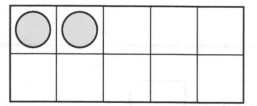

10   ➞ ___ ___

▶ 8 + 4 = ▢

Add.

1   9
   + 3
   12

2   8
   + 6
   14

3   0
   + 5
   0

4   4
   + 4
   8

5   6
   + 7
   12

6   5
   + 2
   7

7   8
   + 1
   9

8   2
   + 9
   11

9 $8 + 8 =$ ___15___

10 $9 + 6 =$ ___15___

11 $8 + 9 =$ ___17___

12 $7 + 4 =$ ___11___

Subtract.

13   8
   − 6
   2

14   9
   − 3
   9

15   12
   − 5
   7

16   11
   − 8
   2

17   9
   − 9
   0

18   13
   − 4
   9

19   14
   − 5
   9

20   11
   − 6
   9

21 13 − 8 = _____

22 15 − 7 = _____

23 12 − 4 = _____

24 18 − 9 = _____

....

25 8 − 0 =

0

⬭

7

⬭

8

⬭

....

26 15 − 9 =

5

⬭

6

⬭

7

⬭

27 CHOOSE The sum of two numbers is 14. What could the two numbers be?

Write an addition fact. _____ + _____ = _____

Write a subtraction fact that is related to your addition fact.

_____ − _____ = _____

What do you notice about the facts you wrote?

Talk about it.

Lesson 4 Odd and Even Numbers

★ You can make pairs with an **even number**.

Here are 16 mittens. They make 8 pairs.
There are no extra mittens.
So 16 is an even number.

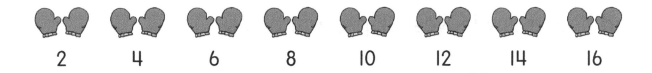

2   4   6   8   10   12   14   16

An even number has 0, 2, 4, 6, or 8 in the ones place.

When you try to make pairs with an **odd number**,
there is always one extra.

Here are 13 socks. The 13 socks make 6 pairs.
There is 1 extra sock.
So 13 is an odd number.

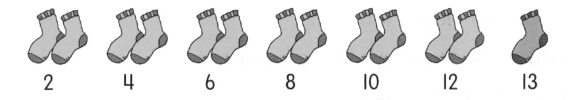

2   4   6   8   10   12   13

An odd number has 1, 3, 5, 7, or 9 in the ones place.

Example 1

How many leaves? Is that number odd or even?

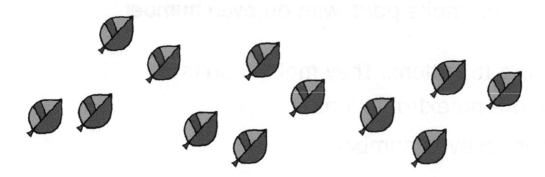

Find how many leaves. Skip-count by 2s.

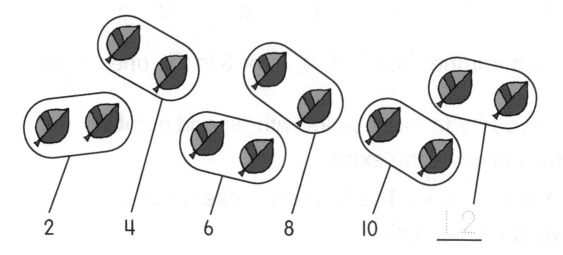

2   4   6   8   10   12

All the leaves are in pairs.

There are no leaves left over.

An odd number always has an extra.

An even number does not.

▶ There are _____ leaves.

The number 12 is an _____ number.

⭐ Every even number can make two equal groups. You can write an equation to show this.

A group of 2 can make two groups of 1.

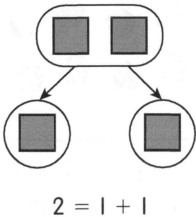

$$2 = 1 + 1$$

A group of 4 can make two groups of 2.

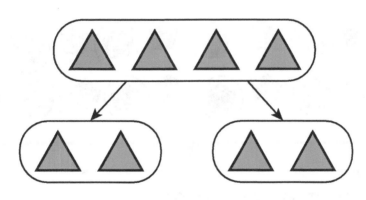

$$4 = 2 + 2$$

A group of 6 can make two groups of 3.

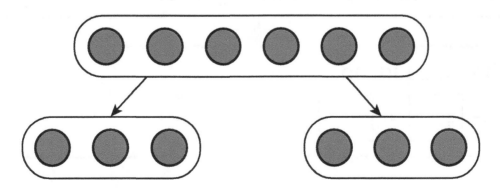

$$6 = 3 + 3$$

Example 2

Write an equation to show that 24 can make
2 equal groups. Use this model to make the groups.

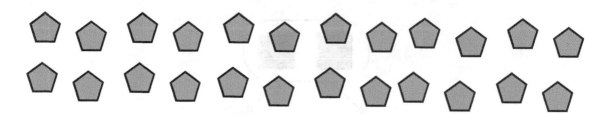

1

To make 2 equal groups, circle every other shape.

There will be I group of circled shapes.

There will be I group of shapes not circled.

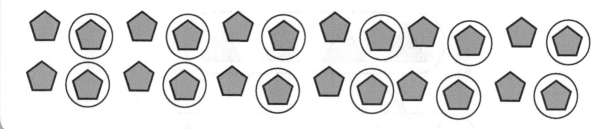

2

Count the shapes you circled.

Count the shapes you did not circle.

There are 12 shapes in each group.

3

Write an equation.

24 = $\boxed{12}$ + $\boxed{12}$

▶ The equation is 24 = _____ + _____.

Camille drew these stars.

How many stars?

Is the number odd or even?

Make pairs of stars.

How many stars are in a pair of stars? ___2___

How many pairs of stars are there? _____

Are there any stars left over? _____

How many stars are there? _____

Is the number of stars odd or even? _____

Write the number.

1

_____ tops

Is the number odd or even? _____

2

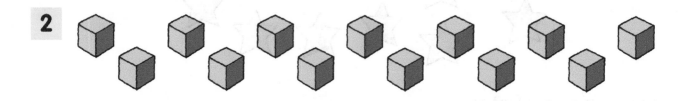

_____ blocks

Is the number odd or even? _____

3

_____ marbles

Is the number odd or even? _____

Finish writing each equation to show that an even number can make 2 equal groups.

4 10 = _____ + _____

5 8 = _____ + _____

6 18 = _____ + _____

7 14 = _____ + _____

8 Which shows an even number of acorns?

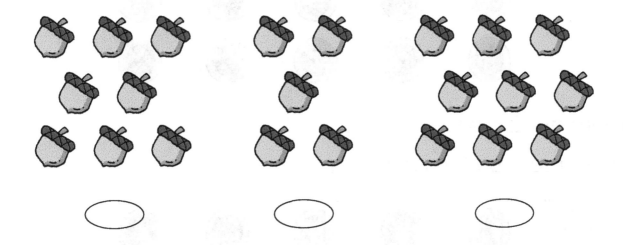

9 **MODEL** Draw a model to show that 22 can be made into 2 equal groups. Then write the equation showing that 22 can have 2 equal addends.

22 = _____ + _____

★ An **array** has rows and columns.
Each row has the same number.
Each column has the same number.

The buttons make an array.

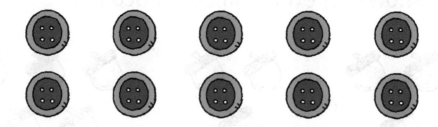

There are 2 rows.

There are 5 buttons in each row.

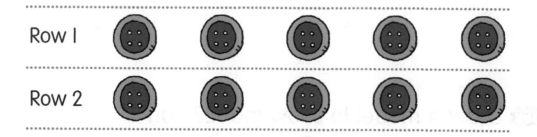

Row 1

Row 2

There are 5 columns.

There are 2 buttons in each column.

| Column 1 | Column 2 | Column 3 | Column 4 | Column 5 |

Example 2

Example 1

How many stars in all?

1. One way is to add the stars in each row.

$$\begin{array}{r} 4 \\ 4 \\ + 4 \\ \hline 12 \end{array}$$

2. Another way is to add the stars in each column.

3 + 3 + 3 + 3 = 12

Both ways, the sum is ____12____.

▶ There are _____ stars in all.

Example 2

How many shapes in all?

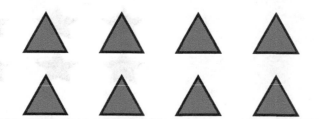

① One way is to add the shapes in each row.

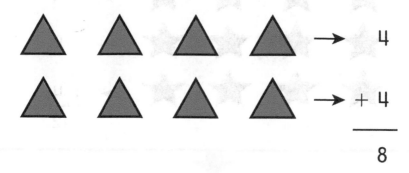

$\rightarrow$ 4

$\rightarrow$ + 4

8

② Another way is to add the shapes in each column.

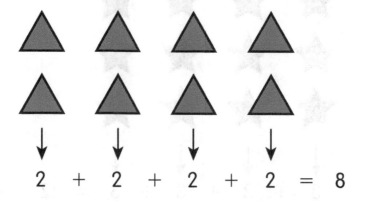

2 + 2 + 2 + 2 = 8

Both ways, the sum is ___8___.

▶ There are _____ shapes in all.

 **Try**

How many cars in all?

1

How many cars are in each row? ___4___

Add the cars in each row.

Write an equation.

___3___ + ___4___ + ___3___ = ___12___

2

How many cars are in each column? _____

Add the cars in each column.

Write an equation.

_____ + _____ + _____ + _____ + = _____

Both ways, the sum is _____.

▶ There are _____ cars in all.

Alexiah

1 How many balls in all?

How many balls in each row? Write an equation.

___3___ + ___3___ = ___6___

There are ___6___ balls in all.

· ·

2 How many stickers in all?

How many stickers in each column?
Write an equation.

___1___ + ___2___ + ___4___ + ___8___ = ___8___

There are ___8___ stickers in all.

3 How many shapes in all?

How many shapes in each row?
Write an equation.

_____ + _____ + _____ + _____ = _____

There are _____ shapes in all.

4 **MODEL** Draw an array that has 5 rows and
4 columns. Use Xs in your drawing.

Write an equation for your array.

_____

How many Xs did you draw in all? _____

1 Shayla has 18 stickers.

Miguel has 9 stickers.

How many stickers do they have in all?

Draw a picture to show how many stickers.

Shayla's stickers	Miguel's stickers

Solve the equation.

$18 + 9 = \boxed{}$

2 Rick had some toy cars. He buys 10 more toy cars. Now he has 35 toy cars in all. How many toy cars did Rick have before?

$$\boxed{} + 10 = 35$$

3 Tara had 26 balloons.
She gave away 10 balloons.
How many balloons were left?

$$26 - 10 = \boxed{}$$

4 Omar had 45 minutes before dinner.
He spent some minutes playing soccer.
Then he had 15 minutes left to walk home.
How many minutes did Omar play soccer?

$$45 - \boxed{} = 15$$

Add. Count on from the greater number.

5 5 + 8 =

5 + 8 = ☐

....

6 3 + 9 =

3 + 9 = ☐

....

Add.

7	9	**8**	0	**9**	8	**10**	3
	+ 9		+ 6		+ 3		+ 7

....

Subtract.

11	14	**12**	18	**13**	13	**14**	4
	− 7		− 7		− 9		− 4

15 8 + 4 =

11 ⬭   12 ⬭   13 ⬭

....

16 9 + 9 =

14 ⬭   16 ⬭   18 ⬭

....

17 7 − 0 =

0 ⬭   7 ⬭   8 ⬭

....

18 15 − 7 =

6 ⬭   7 ⬭   8 ⬭

Write the number.

19

_____ ladybugs in all

Is the number odd or even? _____

20

_____ fish in all

Is the number odd or even? _____

Finish each equation to show that an even number can make 2 equal groups.

21 12 = _____ + _____

22 4 = _____ + _____

23 20 = _____ + _____

24 6 = _____ + _____

....

25 How many frogs in all?

How many frogs in each column?
Write an equation.

_____ + _____ + _____ + _____ + _____ = _____

There are _____ frogs in all.

26 **SOLVE** Lauren had 53 crayons. She gave 20 of them to her friends. Then her mom bought her 16 crayons. How many crayons does Lauren have now?

Write equations and solve the problem.
Show your work.

27 **MODEL** Draw an array that has 4 rows and 3 columns. Use Xs in your drawing.

Write an equation for your array.

_____

How many Xs did you draw in all? _____

A Trip to the Fair

What would you like to ride at the fair?

20 tickets **15 tickets** **5 tickets**

15 tickets **10 tickets**

You have 50 tickets.

You want to use all your tickets.

You can take a ride more than once.

List the rides you would like to take.

_____

_____

How did you decide on your rides?

Talk about it.

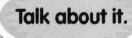

Domain 2
Number and Operations in Base Ten

★ You can show hundreds, tens, and ones as a number.

10 ones make 1 ten.

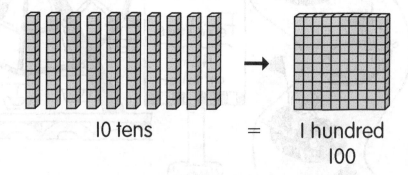

10 ones   =   1 ten
                  10

You can group 10 tens to make 1 hundred.

10 tens   =   1 hundred
                      100

Use a place-value chart to write the number.

Hundreds	Tens	Ones
1	0	0

Example I

What number do the models show?

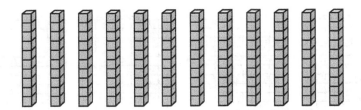

1 Count the tens.

There are 12 tens.

2 Group 10 tens to make 1 hundred.

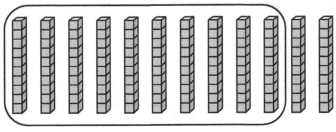

10 tens = 1 hundred   2 tens

3 Write how many hundreds, tens, and ones.

There is 1 hundred. Write 1 in the hundreds column.

There are 2 tens. Write 2 in the tens column.

There are 0 ones. Write 0 in the ones column.

Hundreds	Tens	Ones
1	2	0

▶ The models show the number _____.

Example 2

What number do the models show?

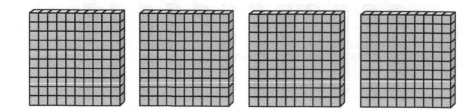

1   Count the hundreds.

There are 4 hundreds.

2   Count the tens and ones.

There are 0 tens.

There are 0 ones.

3   Write how many hundreds, tens, and ones.

Hundreds	Tens	Ones
4	0	0

4   Write the number.

4 hundreds = __400__

▶ The models show the number _____.

Example 3

What number do the models show?

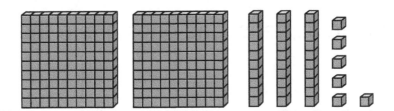

1 Count the hundreds.

There are 2 hundreds.

2 Count the tens.

There are 3 tens.

3 Count the ones.

There are 6 ones.

4 Write the number in a place-value chart.

Hundreds	Tens	Ones
2	3	6

▶ The models show the number _____.

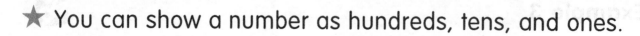

★ You can show a number as hundreds, tens, and ones.

Example 4

How many hundreds, tens, and ones are in the number 518?

1 Write the number in a place-value chart.

Hundreds	Tens	Ones
5	1	8

2 Find how many hundreds.

There are 5 hundreds.

3 Find how many tens.

There is 1 ten.

4 Find how many ones.

There are _____ ones.

▶ The number 518 has

_____ hundreds, _____ ten, and _____ ones.

 **Try**

How many hundreds, tens, and ones are in the number 709?

1 Write the number in a place-value chart.

Hundreds	Tens	Ones
7	0	9

2 Write how many hundreds.

_____ hundreds

3 Write how many tens.

_____ tens

4 Write how many ones.

_____ ones

▶ The number 709 has

_____ hundreds, _____ tens, and _____ ones.

1 How many hundreds, tens, and ones?

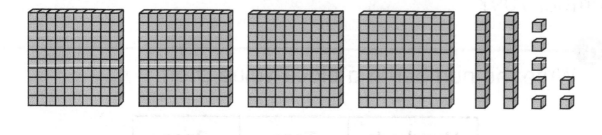

_____ hundreds _____ tens _____ ones

What number do the models show? _____

2 What number do the models show?

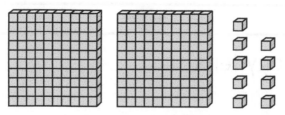

_____

Write how many hundreds, tens, and ones.

3 538

_____ hundreds _____ tens _____ ones

---

4 720

_____ hundreds _____ tens _____ ones

---

5 104

_____ hundred _____ tens _____ones

6 (DRAW) Use models to show the number 407.

How many hundreds, tens, and ones are in the number 407?

_____ hundreds _____ tens _____ ones

⭐ **Skip-count** when groups have the same number.

Skip-count by 5s to find how many leaves in all.

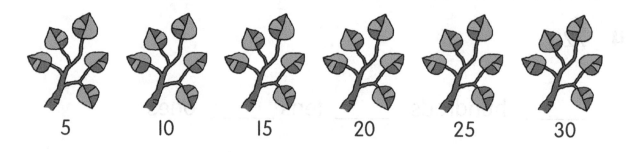

| 5 | 10 | 15 | 20 | 25 | 30 |

The numbers all have 5 or 0 in the ones place.

Skip-count by 10s to find how many crayons in all.

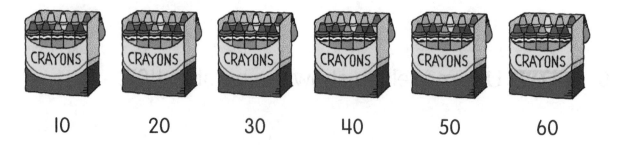

| 10 | 20 | 30 | 40 | 50 | 60 |

The numbers all have 0 in the ones place.

Skip-count by 100s to find how many in all.

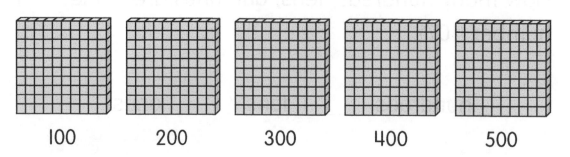

| 100 | 200 | 300 | 400 | 500 |

The numbers all have 0 in the tens and ones places.

Example 1

Start at 5.

Skip-count by 5s to 50.

Use the chart. Color the boxes
as you skip-count by 5s.

List the numbers you count.

1	2	3	4	5	6	7	8	9	10
11	12	13	14	15	16	17	18	19	20
21	22	23	24	25	26	27	28	29	30
31	32	33	34	35	36	37	38	39	40
41	42	43	44	45	46	47	48	49	50

Is there a pattern in the numbers you count?

The numbers you count have a ___5___ or a ___0___ in the ones place.

▶ Skip-counting by 5s, the numbers from 5 to 50 are

5, 10, 15, 20, _____, _____, _____, _____, _____,

and _____.

Example 2

Start at 50. Skip-count by 10s to 100.

Use the chart. Color the boxes
as you skip-count by 10s.

41	42	43	44	45	46	47	48	49	50
51	52	53	54	55	56	57	58	59	60
61	62	63	64	65	66	67	68	69	70
71	72	73	74	75	76	77	78	79	80
81	82	83	84	85	86	87	88	89	90
91	92	93	94	95	96	97	98	99	100

▶ Skip-counting by 10s, the numbers from 50 to 100 are

_____50_____, _____, _____, _____, _____,

and _____.

Example 3

Skip-count by 100s. Write the missing numbers.

500, 600, ___?___, ___?___, 900

The numbers must have 0 in the tens and ones places.

500, 600, __700__, __800__, 900

▶ The missing numbers are _____ and _____.

Start at 200. Skip-count by 5s to 250.

200 —→ 201, 202, 203, 204, **205**

205 —→ 206, 207, 208, 209, **210**

210 —→ 211, 212, 213, 214, **215**

Keep skip-counting by 5s.

200, 205, 210, 215, _220_, _____, _____,

_____, _____, _____, _____

▶ Skip-counting by 5s, the numbers from 200 to 250 are

200, 205, 210, 215, _____, _____, _____,

_____, _____, _____, and _____.

Start at 200 again. Skip-count by 10s to 250.

200 —→ 201, 202, 203, 204, 205, 206, 207, 208, 209, **210**

210 —→ 211, 212, 213, 214, 215, 216, 217, 218, 219, **220**

220 —→ 221, 222, 223, 224, 225, 226, 227, 228, 229, **230**

200, 210, 220, 230, _____, _____

▶ Skip-counting by 10s, the numbers from 200 to 250 are

200, 210, 220, _____, _____, and _____.

1 Each bundle has 10 pencils.
Skip-count by 10s to find how many pencils in all.

How many pencils in all? _____

---

2 Each model stands for 100.
Skip-count by 100s to find how many in all.

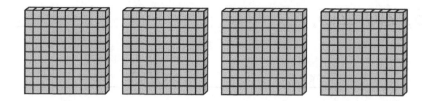

How many in all? _____

---

3 Each pile has 5 coins.
Skip-count by 5s to find how many coins in all.

How many coins in all? _____

4 Start at 40. Skip-count by 10s.

What are the missing numbers?

40, 50, _____, 70, _____, _____, 100

---

5 Start at 200. Skip-count by 100s.

What are the missing numbers?

200, 300, _____, _____, 600, 700,

_____, _____

---

6 Start at 620. Skip-count by 5s.

What are the next three numbers?

620, 625, 630, 635, _____, _____, _____

---

7 COMPARE Start at 800 and skip-count by 5s to 850. Now start at 800 and skip-count by 10s to 850. What do you notice?

Talk about it.

Lesson 8 Reading and Writing Numbers to 1000

★ You use **digits** to write numbers.

The digits you use are 0, 1, 2, 3, 4, 5, 6, 7, 8, and 9.

You use words to read and write **number names**.

Example 1

What is the number name for 735?

1 Write the number in a place-value chart.

Hundreds	Tens	Ones
7	3	5

2 Look at each place.

7 hundreds = 700   Say: _seven hundred_

3 tens =   30   Say: _thirty_

5 ones =   5   Say: _five_

▶ The number name for 735 is

_____.

★ Use place value to find the value of each digit in a number.

Example 2

What is the value of each digit in the number 619?

1

Write the number in a place-value chart.

Hundreds	Tens	Ones
6	1	9

2

Look at the place of each digit in the chart.

The 6 is in the hundreds place.

6 hundreds = 600

The 1 is in the tens place.

1 ten = 10

The 9 is in the ones place.

9 ones = ___9___

▶ In the number 619, the 6 has a value of _____,

the 1 has a value of _____, and the 9 has a value

of _____.

★ A number in **expanded form** shows the value of each digit.

Example 3

Write the number 486 in expanded form.

1 Write the number in a place-value chart.

Hundreds	Tens	Ones
4	8	6

2 Look at the digit in each place.

4 hundreds = 400

8 tens = 80

6 ones = 6

3 Write the values as a sum.

___400___ + ___80___ + ___6___ = 486

▶ The number 486 in expanded form is

_____ + _____ + _____.

What number do the models show?

Write the number in expanded form.

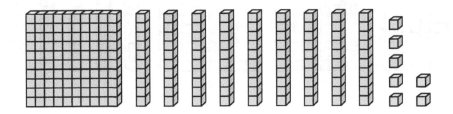

1 Count the models.

_____ hundred   _____ tens   _____ ones

The models show the number _____.

2 Find the value of each digit.

1 hundred = 100   9 tens = _____   7 ones = _____

3 Write the values as a sum.

100 + _____ + _____

▶ The models show the number _____.
The number in expanded form is

_____ + _____ + _____.

1 What number do the models show?

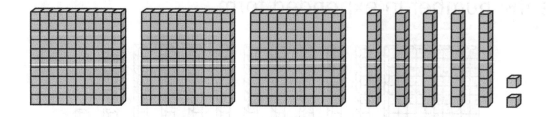

Write the number using digits. _____

Write the number name.

_____

Write the number in expanded form.

_____ + _____ + _____

....

2 What is the value of the 4 in 824?

    400   40   4

....

3 What is the value of the 9 in 902?

    900   90   9

Write the number.

4 nine hundred twenty-three _____

5 four hundred forty-six _____

6 300 + 60 + 2 = _____

7 500 + 10 + 7 = _____

Write the number in expanded form.

8 682 = _____ + _____ + _____

9 435 = _____ + _____ + _____

10 COMPARE Write the number eight hundred nineteen in expanded form.

_____ + _____ + _____

Write the number eight hundred ninety-one in expanded form.

_____ + _____ + _____

How are the expanded forms alike?

How are the expanded forms different?

Talk about it.

★ Use symbols to compare numbers.

The models show 258 and 345.

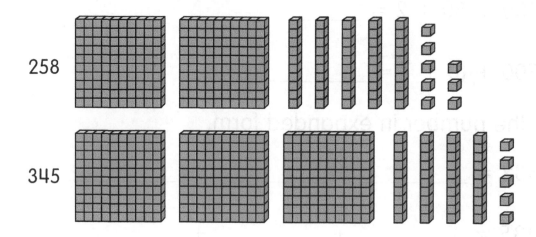

258

345

Compare 258 and 345.

258 has 2 hundreds.

345 has 3 hundreds.

200 is **less than** 300.

258 is less than 345.

$258 < 345$

300 is **greater than** 200.

345 is greater than 258.

$345 > 258$

Numbers that show the same amount are equal.

258 is **equal to** 258.   345 is equal to 345.

$258 = 258$ $345 = 345$

★ Use place value to compare numbers.

Example 1

Compare the numbers. Use >, =, or <.

471 ◯ 468

1

Write the numbers in a place-value chart.

Hundreds	Tens	Ones
4	7	1
4	6	8

2

Compare the hundreds.

4 hundreds = 4 hundreds

The hundreds are the same.

3

Compare the tens.

7 tens is greater than 6 tens.

So 471 is greater than 468.

4

Write >, =, or <.   _____>_____ means is greater than.

▶ 471 ◯ 468

Example 2

Compare the numbers. Use >, =, or <.

604 ◯ 609

1

Compare the hundreds.

<u>6</u>04 has 6 hundreds. <u>6</u>09 has 6 hundreds.

The hundreds are the same.

2

Compare the tens.

6<u>0</u>4 has 0 tens. 6<u>0</u>9 has 0 tens.

The tens are the same.

3

Compare the ones.

60<u>4</u> has 4 ones. 60<u>9</u> has 9 ones.

4 ones is less than 9 ones.

So 604 is less than 609.

4

Write >, =, or <.

_____ means is less than.

▶ 604 ◯ 609

Compare the numbers. Write >, =, or <.

857 ◯ 854

1

Compare the hundreds.

857 has __8__ hundreds. 854 has ____ hundreds.
The hundreds are the same.

2

Compare the tens.

857 has ____ tens. 854 has ____ tens.
The tens are the same.

3

Compare the ones.

857 has ____ ones. 854 has ____ ones.

7 ones is _____ than 4 ones.

So 857 is _____ than 854.

Write >, =, or <.

▶ 857 ◯ 854

Use the models to help you compare.

Write >, =, or <.

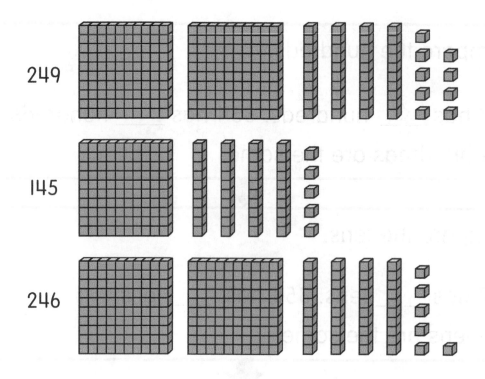

249

145

246

1 249 ◯ 145

2 246 ◯ 145

3 246 ◯ 246

4 145 ◯ 246

5 145 ◯ 249

6 249 ◯ 246

7 246 ◯ 249

8 145 ◯ 145

Write greater than, equal to, or less than to compare.

9 575 is _____ 175.

10 927 is _____ 927.

11 284 is _____ 306.

12 695 is _____ 692.

Compare. Write >, =, or <.

13 394 ◯ 209

14 536 ◯ 536

15 684 ◯ 713

16 499 ◯ 497

17 758 ◯ 761

18 275 ◯ 278

19 143 ◯ 143

20 812 ◯ 807

21 **EXPLAIN** Look at question 18 above. Why did you need to compare the ones?

In what other question above did you need to compare the ones?

Talk about it.

★ Use place value to help you add.

Example 1

$25 + 38 = \boxed{}$

1

Write each addend as tens and ones.

$25 = 2$ tens $+ 5$ ones

$38 = 3$ tens $+ 8$ ones

2

Add the tens.

2 tens $+ 3$ tens $= 5$ tens

3

Add the ones.

5 ones $+ 8$ ones $= 13$ ones

13 ones $= 1$ ten $+ 3$ ones

4

Combine the tens and ones.

5 tens $= 50$

13 ones $= 10 + 3$

$50 + 10 + 3 = \underline{63}$

▶ $25 + 38 = \boxed{}$

Example 2

$75 + 16 = \boxed{}$

 Write each addend as tens and ones.

$75 = 70 + 5$

$16 = 10 + 6$

 Add the tens and ones.

$70 + 5 + 10 + 6$

Add the tens first.

$70 + 10 = 80$

Then add the ones.

$80 + 5 = 85$

$85 + 6 = \underline{91}$

▶ $75 + 16 = \boxed{}$

Example 3

Example 2

```
   37
+ 28
```

1 Add the ones and make a ten.

7 ones + 8 ones = 15 ones

15 ones = 1 ten __5__ ones

Tens	Ones
1 3	7
+ 2	8
	5

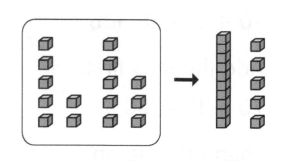

2 Add the tens.

1 ten + 3 tens + 2 tens = __6__ tens

Tens	Ones
1 3	7
+ 2	8
6	5

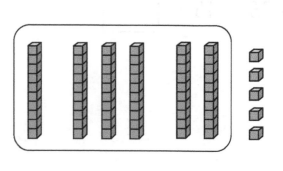

▶
```
   37
+ 28
```

$$\begin{array}{r} 59 \\ + 34 \\ \hline \end{array}$$

1 Add the ones.

9 ones + 4 ones = __13__ ones

2 Make a ten.

13 ones = _____ ten _____ ones

3 Add the tens.

____ ten + ____ tens + ____ tens = ____ tens

	Tens	Ones
	1	
	5	9
+	3	4
		3

▶
$$\begin{array}{r} 59 \\ + 34 \\ \hline \end{array}$$

Write each addend as tens and ones.

Then add.

1   54 + 29 = _____   **2**   36 + 14 = _____

3   81 + 17 = _____   **4**   69 + 23 = _____

5   59 + 21 = _____   **6**   26 + 47 = _____

7   33 + 45 = _____   **8**   16 + 46 = _____

Add.

9

Tens	Ones
3	7
+ 4	8

10

Tens	Ones
5	6
+ 1	6

11

	Tens	Ones
	6	3
+	2	5

12

	Tens	Ones
	7	9
+	1	4

13
```
  39
+ 41
-----
```

14
```
  73
+ 26
-----
```

15
```
  79
+ 11
-----
```

16
```
  37
+ 42
-----
```

17
```
  68
+ 18
-----
```

18
```
  46
+ 17
-----
```

19
```
  56
+ 29
-----
```

20
```
  13
+ 80
-----
```

21 **CHOOSE** Look at the numbers below.
Find two numbers that have a sum of 40.

(33)   (15)   (17)   (25)   (23)

Write an equation.

_____ + _____ = 40

Subtracting Two-Digit Numbers

★ Use different ways to solve a subtraction problem.

Example 1

$74 - 26 =$

ONE WAY

Write the second number as tens and ones.

$26 = 20 + 6$

Subtract the tens.

$74 - 20 = 54$

Subtract the ones.

$54 - 6 = 48$

ANOTHER WAY

Write the second number as a sum of tens and ones.

$26 = 10 + 10 + 6$

Start with 74.

$74 - 10 = 64$

$64 - 10 = 54$

$54 - 6 = \underline{48}$

▶ $74 - 26 =$ ☐

★ Use addition to solve a subtraction problem.

Example 2

$62 - 35 = $ ◼

1

Write a related addition sentence.

35 plus what number equals 62?

$35 + $ ◼ $ = 62$

2

Start with 35. Add until you reach 62.

$35 + 5 = 40$

$40 + 20 = 60$

$60 + 2 = 62$

3

Write the amounts you added.

$5 + 20 + 2$

Find the total. Add the first two numbers.

$5 + 20 = 25$

Then add the third number.

$25 + 2 = 27$

$35 + \boxed{27} = 62$

▶ $62 - 35 = $ ⬜

Example 3

$87 - 53 = \boxed{}$

1

Use models.
Show 87.

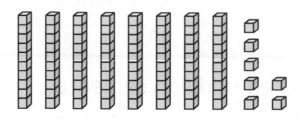

2

Subtract the ones.

7 ones − 3 ones = 4 ones

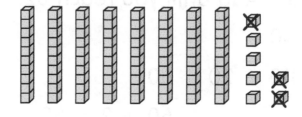

3

Subtract the tens.

8 tens − 5 tens = 3 tens

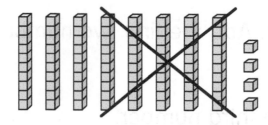

There are 3 tens and 4 ones left.

3 tens 4 ones = ____34____

▶ $87 - 53 = \boxed{}$

Example 4

$43 - 8 =$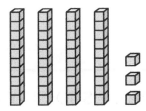

1

Show 43.

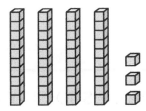

2

There are not enough ones to subtract 8 ones.

Regroup one of the tens as 10 ones.

10 ones + 3 ones = 13 ones

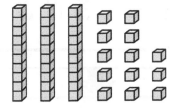

3

Subtract the ones.

13 ones − 8 ones = 5 ones

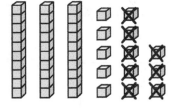

There are 3 tens and 5 ones left.

3 tens 5 ones = _____35_____

▶ 43 − 8 = ☐

Example 5

```
   51
 − 27
```

1

There are not enough ones to subtract 7 ones.

Regroup one of the tens as 10 ones.

Now there are 4 tens and 11 ones.

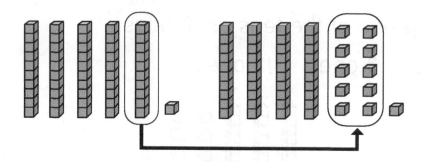

2

Subtract the ones. Then subtract the tens.

Tens	Ones
4	11
5̸	1̸
2	7
2	4

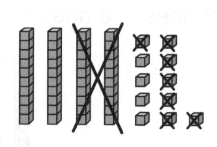

▶
```
   51
 − 27
```

95
− 49

1

There are not enough ones to subtract.

Regroup one of the tens as 10 ones.

Now there are ___8___ tens and ___15___ ones.

	Tens	Ones
	8	15
	9̸	5̸
−	4	9

2

Subtract the ones.

Then subtract the tens.

	Tens	Ones
	8	15
	9̸	5̸
−	4	9

▶ 95
  − 49
  ┌────┐
  │   │
  └────┘

Alexiah

Write the second number as tens and ones.
Then subtract.

1 42 − 16 = ▪

16 = 10 + ____

42 − 10 = ____

____ − ____ = ____

42 − 16 = ☐

2 65 − 27 = ▪

27 = 10 + ____ + ____

65 − 10 = ____

____ − ____ = ____

____ − ____ = ____

65 − 27 = ☐

Write a related addition sentence for each subtraction.
Then add to find the answer.

3 81 − 64 = ▪

64 + ▪ = _____

81 − 64 = ☐

4 79 − 43 = ▪

43 + ▪ = _____

79 − 43 = ☐

Subtract.

5

Tens	Ones
6	3
3	3

− (left of table)

6

Tens	Ones
7	0
4	5

− (left of table)

7   75
     − 24

8   53
     − 6

9   89
     − 11

10   25
      − 16

11   64
      − 35

12   97
      − 29

13   80
      − 54

14   34
      − 15

15   **DECIDE** Circle the equation below that is not correct.

   48 + 10 = 58   48 − 10 = 38

   10 + 48 = 58   10 − 48 = 38

Why is the equation wrong?

Talk about it.

Lesson 12 Adding More than Two Numbers

★ You can add more than two numbers.

Example 1

$17 + 26 + 43 =$

1
Write each addend as tens and ones.

$17 = 10 + 7 \qquad 26 = 20 + 6 \qquad 43 = 40 + 3$

2
Add the tens.

$10 + 20 + 40 \rightarrow$
$$\begin{array}{r} 10 \\ + 20 \\ \hline 30 \end{array} \qquad \begin{array}{r} 30 \\ + 40 \\ \hline 70 \end{array}$$

3
Look at the ones.
Change the order
to make 10.

$7 + 6 + 3 = 7 + 3 + 6$

4
Add the ones.
Group 2 addends.

$7 + 3 = 10$

$10 + 6 = 16$

5
Combine the tens and ones.

$70 + 16 =$ _86_

▶ $17 + 26 + 43 =$ ☐

Example 2

Example 3

$22 + 36 + 16 + 23 =$ ▢

1

Write each addend as tens and ones.

22	36	16	23
↓	↓	↓	↓
20 + 2	30 + 6	10 + 6	20 + 3

2

Add the tens.

$20 + 30 + 10 + 20 \rightarrow$

$$\begin{array}{c} 20 \\ + 30 \\ \hline 50 \end{array} \nearrow \begin{array}{c} 50 \\ + 10 \\ \hline 60 \end{array} \nearrow \begin{array}{c} 60 \\ + 20 \\ \hline 80 \end{array}$$

3

Add the ones. First add the double.

$2 + 6 + 6 + 3$

$2 + \quad 12 \quad + 3 \quad \rightarrow \quad 2 + 12 = 14$

$14 + 3 = 17$

4

Combine the tens and ones.

$80 + 17 =$ _97_

▶ $22 + 36 + 16 + 23 =$ ▢

Example 3

```
   25
   34
+  16
```

1

Add the ones.

First add 4 ones and 6 ones.

4 ones + 6 ones = 10 ones

10 ones + 5 ones = 15 ones

Make a ten.

15 ones = 1 ten 5 ones

	Tens	Ones
	1	
	2	5
	3	4
+	1	6
		5

2

Add the tens.

1 ten + 2 tens = 3 tens

3 tens + 3 tens = 6 tens

6 tens + 1 ten = __7__ tens

	Tens	Ones
	1	
	2	5
	3	4
+	1	6
	7	5

```
   25
   34
+  16
```

12 + 45 + 28 + 13 = ▮

1

Add the ones.

First add 2 ones and 8 ones.

2 ones + 8 ones = 10 ones

10 ones + 5 ones = 15 ones

15 ones + 3 ones = 18 ones

Make a ten.

18 ones = __1__ ten __8__ ones

Tens	Ones
1	
1	2
4	5
2	8
+ 1	3
	8

2

Add the tens.

1 ten + 1 ten = 2 tens

2 tens + 4 tens = 6 tens

6 tens + 2 tens = 8 tens

8 tens + 1 ten = 9 tens

Tens	Ones
1	
1	2
4	5
2	8
+ 1	3
	8

▶ 12 + 45 + 28 + 13 = ▯

Write each addend as tens and ones.

Then add.

1 26 + 14 + 33 = _____

2 43 + 27 + 18 = _____

3 38 + 21 + 14 + 12 = _____

4 28 + 42 + 18 + 11 = _____

Add.

5

Tens	Ones
4	1
1	9
+ 2	7

6

Tens	Ones
1	6
2	5
3	5
+ 1	4

7	17	**8**	13	**9**	28	**10**	25
	39		9		15		12
	+ 41		+ 26		22		15
					+ 11		+ 42

11 27 + 14 + 47 = _____

12 45 + 13 + 23 = _____

13 **IDENTIFY** Find the missing addend.

35 + 21 + ▒ = 94

35 + 21 + ☐ = 94

How did you find the missing addend?

Talk about it.

★ You can add numbers that have three digits.

Example 1

153 + 241 = ▢

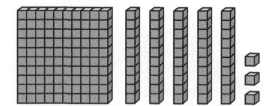

153

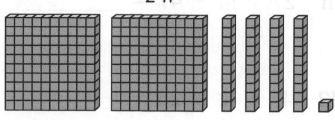

241

① Add the ones.

3 ones + 1 one = 4 ones

② Add the tens.

5 tens + 4 tens = 9 tens

③ Add the hundreds.

1 hundred + 2 hundreds = 3 hundreds

④ Find the sum.

3 hundreds + 9 tens + 4 ones = 300 + 90 + 4

300 + 90 + 4 = _395_

▶ 153 + 241 = ▢

Example 2

Example 2

$327 + 219 = \boxed{}$

① Add the ones.

7 ones + 9 ones = 16 ones

Regroup.

16 ones = 1 ten 6 ones

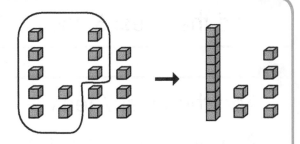

② Add the tens.

Start with the ten you made from 16 ones.

1 ten + 2 tens + 1 ten = 4 tens

③ Add the hundreds.

3 hundreds + 2 hundreds = 5 hundreds

④ Find the sum.

5 hundreds + 4 tens + 6 ones = 500 + 40 + 6

500 + 40 + 6 = __546__

▶ $327 + 219 = \boxed{}$

Example 3

$175 + 264 = \boxed{}$

 1

Add the ones: 5 ones + 4 ones = 9 ones

2

Add the tens: 7 tens + 6 tens = 13 tens

Regroup. 13 tens = 1 hundred 3 tens

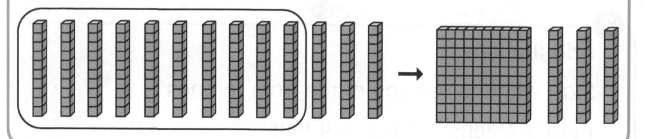

3

Add the hundreds.

Start with the hundred you regrouped from 13 tens.

1 hundred + 1 hundred + 2 hundreds = 4 hundreds

4

Find the sum.

4 hundreds + 3 tens + 9 ones = 400 + 30 + 9

$400 + 30 + 9 = \underline{439}$

▶ $175 + 264 = \boxed{}$

Example 4

$672 + 184 = $ ▢

1

Add the ones: 2 ones + 4 ones = 6 ones

Add the tens: 7 tens + 8 tens = 15 tens

Regroup. 15 tens = 1 hundred 5 tens

	Hundreds	Tens	Ones
	1		
	6	7	2
+	1	8	4
		5	6

2 Add the hundreds.

	Hundreds	Tens	Ones
	1		
	6	7	2
+	1	8	4
	8	5	6

▶ $672 + 184 = $ ▢

$350 + 198 = \blacksquare$

1

Add the ones.

Add the tens.

Regroup.

14 tens = _____ hundred _____ tens

Hundreds	Tens	Ones
☐		
3	5	0
+ 1	9	8
		8

2

Add the hundreds.

Hundreds	Tens	Ones
1		
3	5	0
+ 1	9	8
	4	8

▶ $350 + 198 = \boxed{}$

1 291 + 235 = ▢

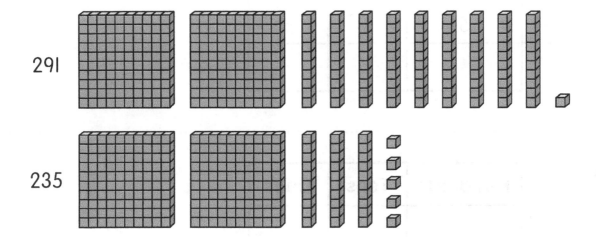

291 + 235 = ▢

2

	Hundreds	Tens	Ones
	7	3	1
+	2	4	5

3

Hundreds	Tens	Ones
3	5	8
+ 5	2	6

4

Hundreds	Tens	Ones
2	5	7
+ 3	8	1

5 **EXPLAIN** There are 347 science books in the library. There are 281 sports books in the library. How many science books and sports books are in the library in all?

Solve the problem.

How did you find your answer?

Talk about it.

Lesson 14 Subtracting Three-Digit Numbers

★ You can subtract numbers with three digits.

Example 1

348 − 125 = ▢

1 Subtract the ones.

8 ones − 5 ones = 3 ones

2 Subtract the tens.

4 tens − 2 tens = 2 tens

3 Subtract the hundreds.

3 hundreds − 1 hundred = 2 hundreds

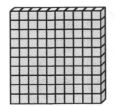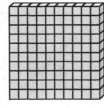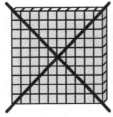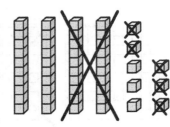

There are 2 hundreds, 2 tens, and 3 ones left.

200 + 20 + 3 = _223_

▶ 348 − 125 = ▢

Example 2

$273 - 146 = \boxed{}$

1

Subtract the ones.

There are not enough ones to subtract 6 ones.

Regroup one of the tens as 10 ones.

10 ones + 3 ones = 13 ones

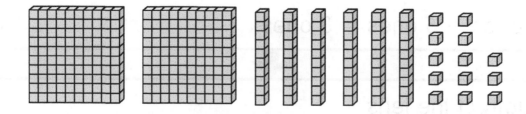

2

Subtract the ones: 13 ones − 6 ones = 7 ones

Subtract the tens: 6 tens − 4 tens = 2 tens

Subtract the hundreds:

2 hundreds − 1 hundred = 1 hundred

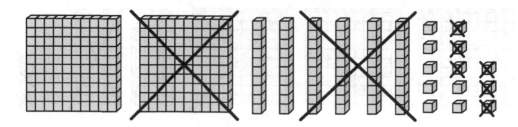

There are 1 hundred, 2 tens, and 7 ones left.

100 + 20 + 7 = ___127___

▶ 273 − 146 = ☐

Example 3

$314 - 152 = $

 Subtract the ones: 4 ones − 2 ones = 2 ones

2

There are not enough tens to subtract 5 tens.

Regroup one of the hundreds as 10 tens.

10 tens + 1 ten = 11 tens

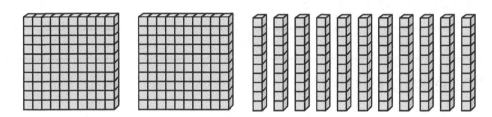

3

Continue subtracting.

Subtract the tens: 11 tens − 5 tens = 6 tens

Subtract the hundreds:

2 hundreds − 1 hundred = 1 hundred

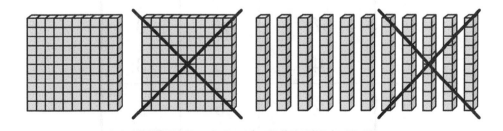

There are 1 hundred, 6 tens, and 2 ones left.

$100 + 60 + 2 = \underline{162}$

▶ $314 - 152 = \boxed{}$

Example 4

728 − 463 = ▨

1

Subtract the ones.
There are not enough
tens to subtract.

Regroup one of the
hundreds as 10 tens.

Now there are 12 tens.

Hundreds	Tens	Ones
6	12	
7̸	2̸	8
− 4	6	3
		5

2

Continue subtracting.

Subtract the tens: 12 tens − 6 tens = __6__ tens

Subtract the hundreds:

6 hundreds − 4 hundreds = __2__ hundreds

Hundreds	Tens	Ones
6	12	
7̸	2̸	8
− 4	6	3
2	6	5

▶ 728 − 463 = ☐

$569 - 182 = \boxed{}$

1

Subtract the ones.
There are not enough
tens to subtract.

Regroup one of the
hundreds as 10 tens.

Now there are 16 tens.

Hundreds	Tens	Ones
$\boxed{}$	$\boxed{}$	
5̸	6̸	9
− 1	8	2
		7

2

Continue subtracting.

Subtract the tens.

Subtract the hundreds.

Hundreds	Tens	Ones
4	16	
5̸	6̸	9
− 1	8	2
		7

▶ $569 - 182 = \boxed{}$

1 254 − 108 = ▢

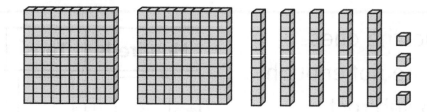

254 − 108 = ▢

---

2 326 − 150 = ▢

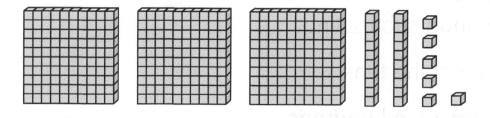

326 − 150 = ▢

3

Hundreds	Tens	Ones
6	7	9
− 3	5	2

4

Hundreds	Tens	Ones
7	4	8
− 2	1	9
5	3	0

5

Hundreds	Tens	Ones
8	1	7
− 4	2	5
4	0	2

tens | ones
7 | 6
8 | 0

6 **EXPLAIN** Amelia has read 283 pages of a book. Tim has read 176 pages of the same book. How many more pages of the book has Amelia read than Tim?

Solve the problem.

How did you find your answer?

Talk about it.

★ You can use mental math to add or subtract 10 or 100.

Example 1

Find the sum: 385 + 10 = ▢

When you add 10, the tens digit changes.

Hundreds	Tens	Ones
3	**8**	5

Hundreds	Tens	Ones
3	9	5

▶ 385 + 10 = ▢

Example 2

Find the difference: 385 − 10 = ▢

When you subtract 10, the tens digit changes.

Hundreds	Tens	Ones
3	**8**	5

Hundreds	Tens	Ones
3	7	5

▶ 385 − 10 = ▢

Example 3

Find the sum: 385 + 100 = ▢

When you add 100, the
hundreds digit changes.

Hundreds	Tens	Ones
3	8	5

Hundreds	Tens	Ones
4	8	5

▶ 385 + 100 = ▢

Example 4

Find the difference: 385 − 100 = ▢

When you subtract 100, the
hundreds digit changes.

Hundreds	Tens	Ones
3	8	5

Hundreds	Tens	Ones
2	8	5

▶ 385 − 100 = ▢

Example 5

Find the sum: 694 + 10 = ▢

When you add 10 to 694, both the tens and hundreds digits change.

Hundreds	Tens	Ones
6	9	4

Hundreds	Tens	Ones
7	0	4

▶ 694 + 10 = ▢

Example 6

Find the difference: 806 − 10 = ▢

When you subtract 10 from 806, both the tens and hundreds digits change.

Hundreds	Tens	Ones
8	0	6

Hundreds	Tens	Ones
7	9	6

▶ 806 − 10 = ▢

Find the difference: 602 − 10 =

Use place value.

602 = 6 hundreds _____ tens 2 ones

To subtract 10 from 602, change 1 hundred to _____ tens.

602 = 5 hundreds _____ tens 2 ones

10 tens − 1 ten = _____ tens

So 602 − 10 = _____ hundreds _____ tens 2 ones.

When you subtract 10 from 602, which digits change?

_____

Which digit stays the same? _____

▶ 602 − 10 = ☐

Practice

Add 10.

1 $354 + 10 =$ _____

2 $698 + 10 =$ _____

3 $735 + 10 =$ _____

4 $929 + 10 =$ _____

Subtract 10.

5 $297 - 10 =$ _____

6 $456 - 10 =$ _____

7 $573 - 10 =$ _____

8 $202 - 10 =$ _____

Add 100.

9 $270 + 100 =$ _____

10 $306 + 100 =$ _____

11 $791 + 100 =$ _____

12 $517 + 100 =$ _____

Subtract 100.

13 $403 - 100 =$ _____

14 $522 - 100 =$ _____

15 $364 - 100 =$ _____

16 $810 - 100 =$ _____

Add or subtract.

17 275 + 10 = _____

18 398 + 100 = _____

19 709 − 10 = _____

20 406 + 100 = _____

21 691 − 100 = _____

22 817 − 10 = _____

23 911 − 10 = _____

24 594 + 10 = _____

25 **TELL** Nadia counted 318 words on a page that she read. Al counted 308 words on a page that he read.

Who counted fewer words?

_____ counted fewer words.

How many fewer words did that person count?

_____ fewer words

1 What number equals 10 tens?

Write the word name. Then write the number.

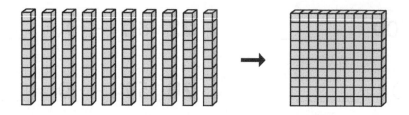

10 tens = _____

Write the number. _____

2 How many hundreds, tens, and ones?

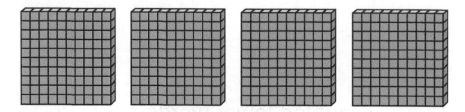

_____ hundreds _____ tens _____ ones

What number do the models show? _____

3 Use models to show the number 217.

How many hundreds, tens, and ones are in the number 217?

_____ hundreds _____ ten _____ ones

....

4 Each bundle has 10 pencils.

Skip-count by 10s to find how many pencils in all.

How many pencils in all? _____

....

5 Start at 60. Skip-count by 5s.

What are the next three numbers?

60, 65, 70, 75, _____, _____, _____

6 Start at 200. Skip-count by 100s.

What are the next three numbers?

200, 300, 400, 500, _____, _____, _____

· ·

7 What number do the models show?

Write the number using digits.

_____

Write the number name.

_____

Write the number in expanded form.

_____ + _____ + _____

Compare.

8 297 299

     >   =   <

$\bigcirc$ $\bigcirc$ $\bigcirc$

9 302 301

     >   =   <

$\bigcirc$ $\bigcirc$ $\bigcirc$

10 568 568

     >   =   <

$\bigcirc$ $\bigcirc$ $\bigcirc$

Write a related addition sentence for each subtraction.
Then add to find the answer.

11 $72 - 53 = \blacksquare$ **12** $49 - 24 = \blacksquare$

     $53 + \blacksquare = \rule{2cm}{0.4pt}$ $24 + \blacksquare = \rule{2cm}{0.4pt}$

     $72 - 53 = \boxed{}$ $49 - 24 = \boxed{}$

Add.

13 25
  + 32
____

14 63
  + 26
____

15 59
  + 18
____

16 35
  + 45
____

....

Subtract.

17 83
  − 51
____

18 46
  − 22
____

19 64
  − 9
____

20 37
  − 18
____

....

Add.

21 12
   35
  + 52
____

22 22
    8
  + 43
____

23 15
   20
   31
  + 16
____

24 39
   11
   12
  + 27
____

25 243 + 328 =

243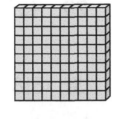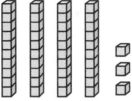

328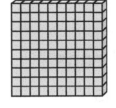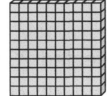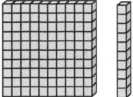

243 + 328 = ☐

....

Subtract.

26

Hundreds	Tens	Ones
7	8	5
− 3	4	5

27

Hundreds	Tens	Ones
8	4	2
− 6	3	9

Use mental math. Add or subtract.

28 $252 + 10 =$ _____

29 $465 + 100 =$ _____

30 $604 - 10 =$ _____

31 $818 - 100 =$ _____

32 (FIND) Mrs. Riva's class collected 237 cans.
Mr. Stewart's class collected 314 cans.
How many cans did the classes collect in all?

Solve the problem. Show your work.

Why do you think your
answer is correct?

Talk about it.

Kittens for Sale

The Cat Care Society has kittens to sell.

Use the clues to find how many kittens were sold.

Clue 1 There were 101 kittens for sale.

Clue 2 Emily sold 15 kittens. Then she sold 18 more kittens.

Clue 3 Evan sold 12 kittens. Then he sold 25 more kittens.

Clue 4 Anna sold 10 fewer kittens than Evan.

Emily Sold	Evan Sold	Anna Sold
_____ kittens	_____ kittens	_____ kittens

How many kittens are still for sale? _____ kittens

Show your work and explain your answer.

Talk about it.

Domain 3
Measurement and Data

Domain 3
Measurement and Data

How many inches longer is the blue shark than the orange clownfish?

Lesson 16 Measuring Length: Inches and Feet

★ **Length** tells you how long something is.

An **inch** ruler can help you find the length of short objects.

Use a yardstick or tape measure to find the length of longer objects.

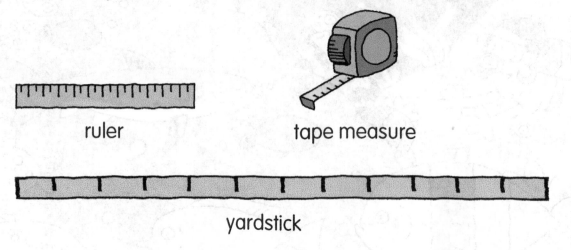

ruler   tape measure

yardstick

Use an inch ruler to measure the length of this ribbon.

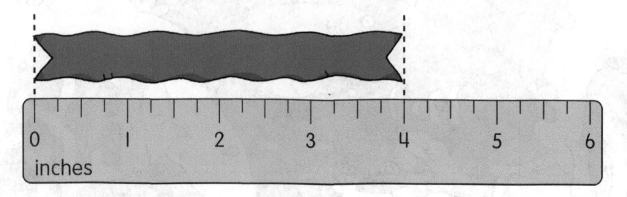

First, line up one end of the ribbon with the 0-mark on the ruler.

Then, read the number of inches that lines up with the other end of the ribbon.

The ribbon is 4 inches long.

Example 1

How many inches long is the straw?

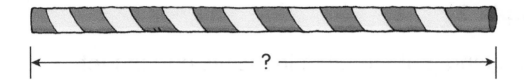

Use an inch ruler to measure.

1 Line up one end of the straw with the 0-mark on the ruler.

2 Read the number on the ruler at the other end of the straw.

The number that lines up with the other end of the straw is at the ___5___-inch mark.

▶ The straw is _____ inches long.

★ A length of 12 inches is the same as 1 **foot**.
A length of 36 inches is the same as 3 feet or 1 **yard**.

Example 2

Find the length of the table in inches and in feet.

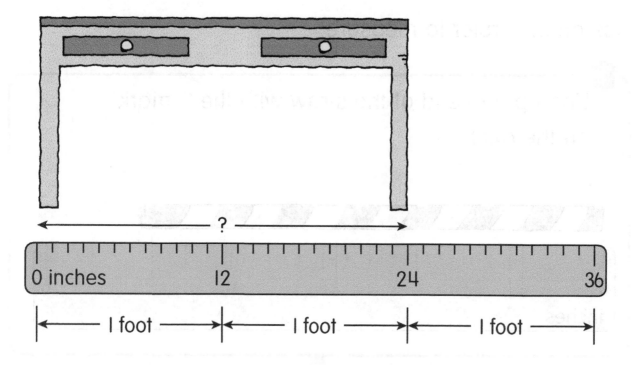

Line up the 0-mark on the yardstick with one end of the table.

The other end of the table lines up with the ___24___-inch mark on the yardstick.

The other end of the table also lines up with the ___2___-foot mark.

▶ The table is _____ inches long.

The table is _____ feet long.

Use the picture of the yardstick. Find the length of the cabinet in inches, in feet, and in yards.

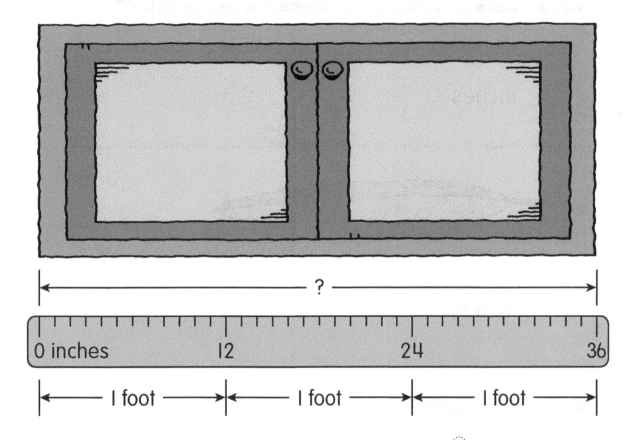

One end of the cabinet lines up with the _____-mark on the yardstick.

The other end of the cabinet lines up with the mark

for _____ inches and the mark for _____ feet.

▶ The cabinet is _____ inches long.

It is also _____ feet long.

These lengths are the same as _____ yard.

Use an inch ruler to measure each object.

1

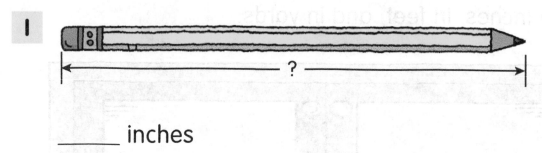

_____ inches

2

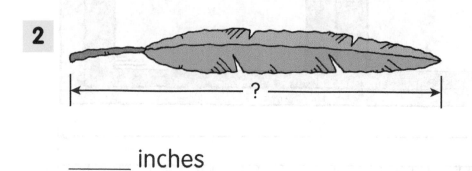

_____ inches

3

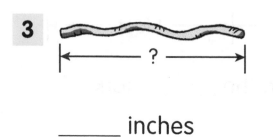

_____ inches

4

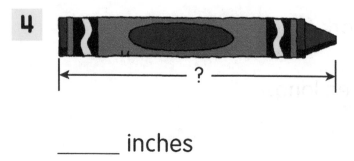

_____ inches

5 Which of these would you measure with a yardstick?

a lady bug   a tennis ball   a car

◯   ◯   ◯

6 **PROVE** Ralph says that 17 inches is the same as 1 foot 6 inches.

Is Ralph correct?

How do you know?

Talk about it.

Use the picture of the yardstick to help you explain your answer.

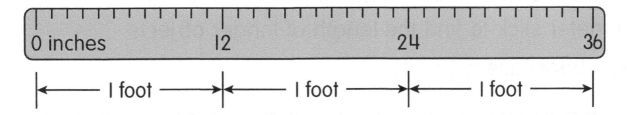

**Measuring Length:
Centimeters and Meters**

★ You can also use a **centimeter** ruler to find
   the length of short objects. Your finger
   is about 1 centimeter wide.

The ruler below shows centimeters.

The leaf is 4 centimeters long.

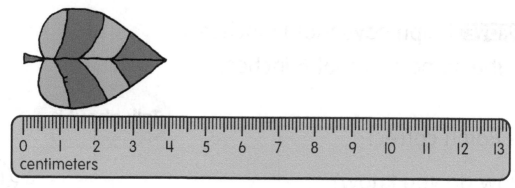

centimeter ruler

There are 100 centimeters in 1 **meter**.

A meter stick is 100 centimeters long. You can use
a meter stick to find the length of longer objects.

The bookcase is 1 meter long.

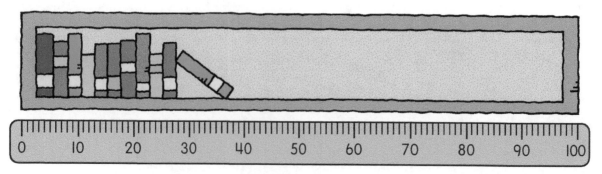

meter stick

Example

How many centimeters long is the pen?

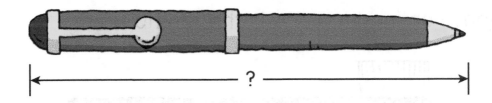

Use a centimeter ruler to measure.

1

Line up one end of the pen with the 0-mark on the ruler.

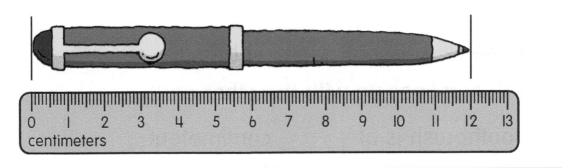

2

Read the number on the ruler that lines up with the other end of the pen.

The number that lines up with the other end is at __12__ centimeters.

▶ The pen is _____ centimeters long.

Use a centimeter ruler. Measure the toothbrush.

How many centimeters long is the toothbrush?

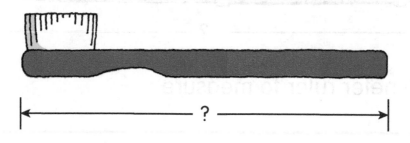

Line up one end of the toothbrush with

the _____-mark on the ruler.

Look at the other end of the toothbrush.

The mark that lines up with the other end

of the toothbrush is at _____ centimeters.

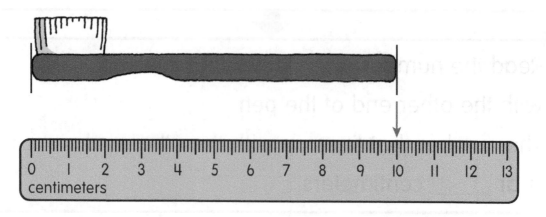

▶ The toothbrush is _____ centimeters long.

Use a centimeter ruler to measure each object.

1

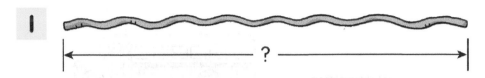

_____ centimeters

2

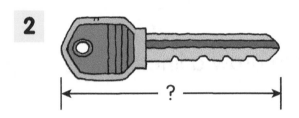

_____ centimeters

3

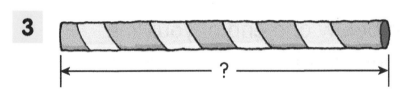

_____ centimeters

4

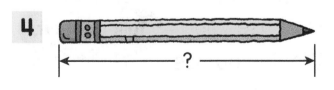

_____ centimeters

5 Which length would you measure with a centimeter ruler?

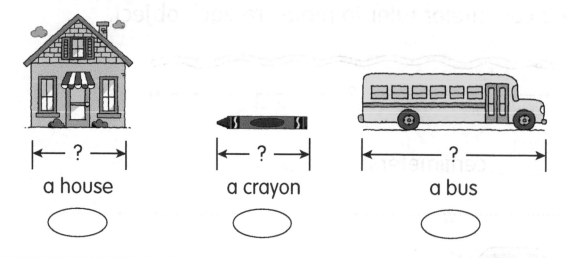

| a house | a crayon | a bus |

6 **PROVE** Use a centimeter ruler to draw a line that is 1 centimeter long.

Line up an inch ruler below one end of your line. Draw a line that is 1 inch long.

Compare your lines.
Which line is longer? _____

Suppose you measure the length of your classroom in inches. Then suppose you measure it in centimeters. Would you use more inches or more centimeters?

Talk about it.

Lesson 18 Measuring with Different Units

★ You can measure the same length with different-size units.

Example 1

Does it take more inches or more feet to measure the length of the bookshelf?

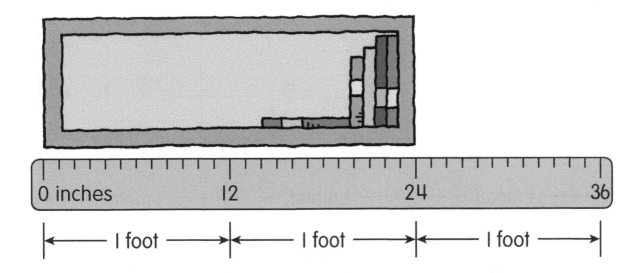

How many inches long is the bookshelf? __24__ inches

How many feet long is the bookshelf? __2__ feet

▶ Inches are smaller than feet. So it takes more

_____ than _____

to measure the bookshelf.

Example 2

Kim drew this picture of her bedroom.
Does it take more centimeters or more meters
to measure the length of the bedroom?

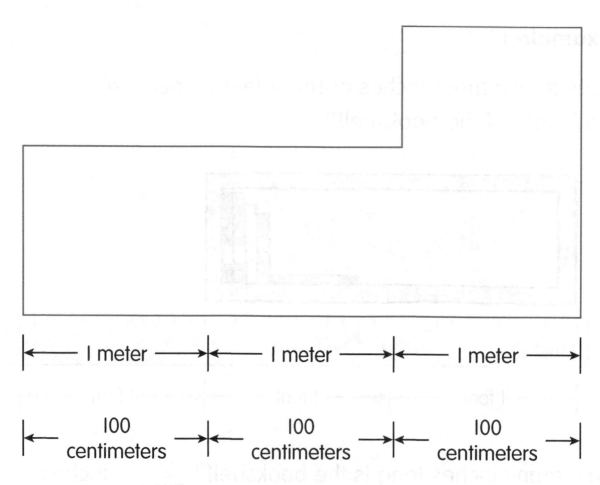

How many centimeters long is Kim's bedroom?

__300__ centimeters

How many meters long is the bedroom? __3__ meters

▶ It takes more _____ than _____
to measure the length of Kim's bedroom.

Does it take more inches or more centimeters
to measure the length of a pencil?

1 Use an inch ruler to measure this pencil.

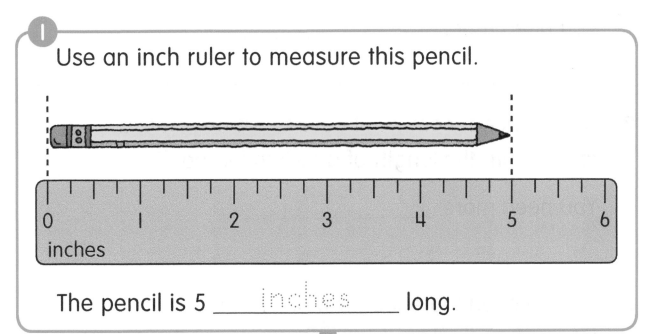

The pencil is 5 _____inches_____ long.

2 Use a centimeter ruler to measure the same pencil.

The pencil is almost 13 _____centimeters_____ long.

▶ It takes more _____ than _____
to measure the length of the pencil.

1   Do you need more inches or more feet
to measure the length of a sofa?

You need more _____.

---

2   Do you need more centimeters or more meters
to measure the length of a swimming pool?

You need more _____.

---

3   Do you need more feet or more yards
to measure the length of your classroom?

You need more _____.

---

4   Do you need more inches or more yards
to measure the length of a football field?

You need more _____.

---

5   Do you need more inches or more centimeters
to measure the length of a rope?

You need more _____.

6 Do you need more yards or more centimeters to measure the height of a building?

You need more _____.

---

7 Do you need more centimeters or more feet to measure the height of your classroom?

You need more _____.

---

8 Do you need more inches or more meters to measure the length of your house?

You need more _____.

---

9 **EXPLAIN** Which measurement is longer, 10 inches or 10 centimeters?

_____

How do you know?

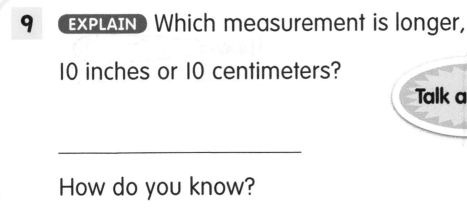
Talk about it.

★ When you **estimate** the length of an object, you tell *about* how long it is.

An eraser is about
2 inches long.

One side of this book is
a little less than 1 foot long.

Your thumb is about
1 centimeter wide.

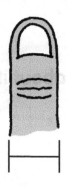

A baseball bat is about
1 meter long.

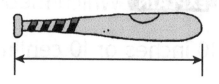

You can use a 1-inch line and a 1-centimeter line
to estimate the length of short objects.

1 inch   1 centimeter

Estimate the length. Then measure with a ruler.
Check to see if your estimate makes sense.

About how many inches long is the yarn?

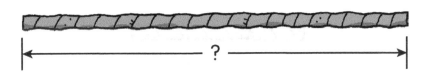

─────── ? ───────

1 Estimate the length. Use the 1-inch line to help.

─────

────── ────── ────── ──────

The yarn is about four 1-inch lines long.

2 Use an inch ruler to measure the length.

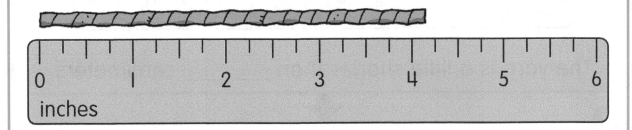

The yarn is a little longer than 4 inches.

3 Compare your measurement to your estimate.

The estimated length was 4 inches.

The measured length was close to _____ inches.

▶ The yarn is about _____ inches long.

Estimate the length of the yarn in centimeters.

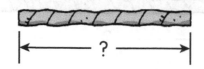

1. To help estimate, think about a 1-centimeter line.

   The yarn is about ___5___ 1-centimeter lines long.

2. Measure the length. Use a centimeter ruler.

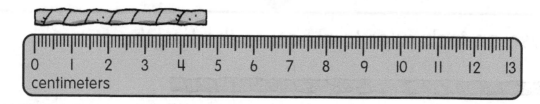

   The yarn is a little shorter than _____ centimeters.

3. Compare your measurement to your estimate.

   The estimated length was about _____ centimeters.

   The measured length was about _____ centimeters.

▶ A good estimate for the length of the yarn is

about _____ centimeters.

Practice

Estimate the length. Then use a ruler to measure.

1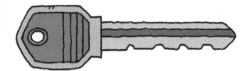

estimate: _____ inches

measurement: _____ inches

2

estimate: _____ centimeters

measurement: _____ centimeters

3 Suppose the orange strip is 1 foot long.
About how many feet long is the desk?

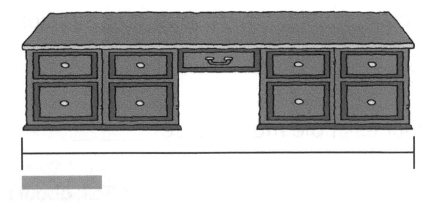

The desk is about _____ feet long.

4 Suppose the table is 2 feet tall. About how tall is Jessica?

Jessica is about _____ feet tall.

5 **TELL** Estimate the length of one of your shoes.

estimate: _____

Now measure the length of the shoe from the tip of the toe to the back of the heel.

measurement: _____

Is your estimated length close to your measured length?

_____

Does your estimate make sense? _____

Talk about it.

Lesson 20 # Finding the Difference between Lengths

★ You can find how much longer one object is than another.

Example 1

How many inches longer than the crayon is the feather?

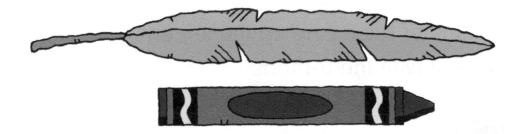

Use an inch ruler. Line up one end of each object with the 0-mark.

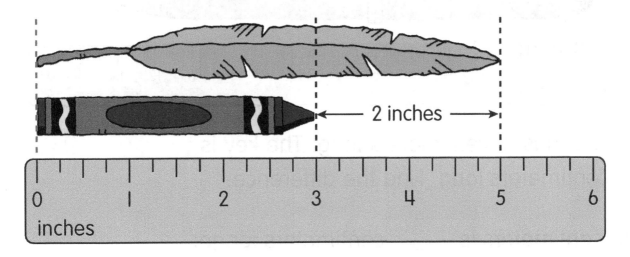

The feather is 5 inches long. The crayon is 3 inches long. Find the difference.

5 inches is __2__ inches longer than 3 inches.

▶ The feather is _____ inches longer than the crayon.

Example 2

How many centimeters longer is the pen than the key?

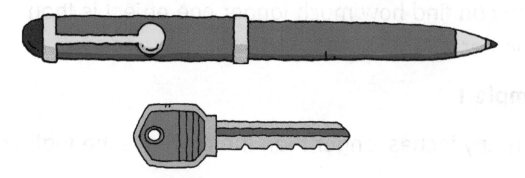

Use a centimeter ruler. Line up the left end of each object with the 0-mark.

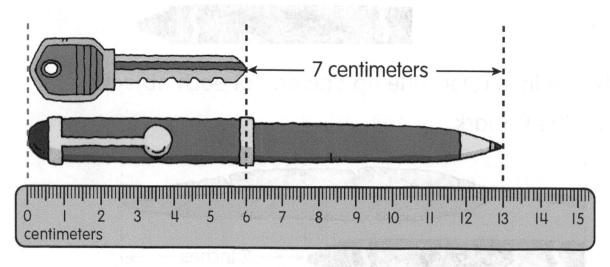

The pen is 13 centimeters long. The key is 6 centimeters long. Find the difference.

13 centimeters is __7__ centimeters longer than 6 centimeters.

▶ The pen is _____ centimeters longer than the key.

 Try

How many centimeters longer is the green yarn than the blue yarn?

Use a centimeter ruler. Line up one end of each piece of yarn with the _____-mark on the ruler.

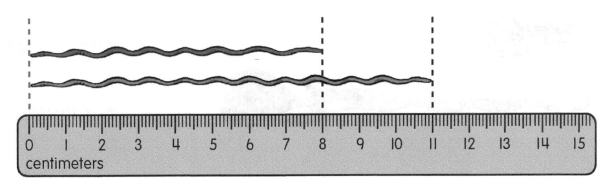

The blue yarn is _____ centimeters long.

The green yarn is _____ centimeters long.

Find the difference.

11 centimeters is _____ centimeters longer than 8 centimeters.

▶ The green yarn is _____ centimeters longer than the blue yarn.

Measure each object.

Find the difference between the lengths.

Write how much longer.

1 Use a centimeter ruler. How much longer than the yellow flower is the red flower?

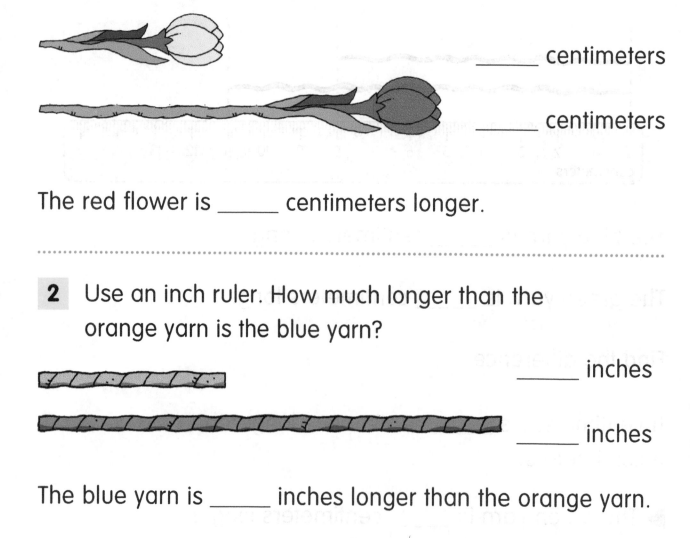

_____ centimeters

_____ centimeters

The red flower is _____ centimeters longer.

2 Use an inch ruler. How much longer than the orange yarn is the blue yarn?

_____ inches

_____ inches

The blue yarn is _____ inches longer than the orange yarn.

3 How many centimeters longer than the crayon is the pencil?

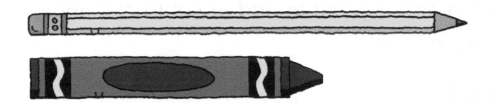

The pencil is _____ centimeters longer than the crayon.

4 **TELL** Use an inch ruler to measure each object.

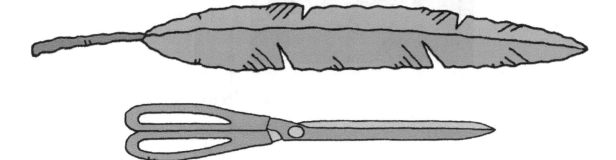

The feather is _____ inches long.

The scissors are _____ inches long.

Which object is longer? How much longer?

The _____ is _____ inches longer than the

_____.

How did you line up each object with the ruler?

Talk about it.

★ Sometimes you need to add or subtract lengths to solve a problem.

| Example 1 | |

Jodie's blue curtain was 24 inches long. She added 18 inches of pink material to the bottom. Then what was the total length of the curtain?

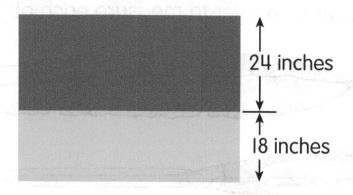

24 inches

18 inches

1 Write an equation to show the problem.

Find the sum of 24 inches and 18 inches.

24 + 18 = ▨

2 Solve.
$$\begin{array}{r} 24 \\ +18 \\ \hline 42 \end{array}$$ ← total length

▶ The total length of the curtain was _____ inches.

Example 2

Brad had a board that was 96 centimeters long. He cut off a piece that was 18 centimeters long. He used the part that was left as a shelf. How long was the shelf?

1 Draw a picture to show the board. Label the parts.

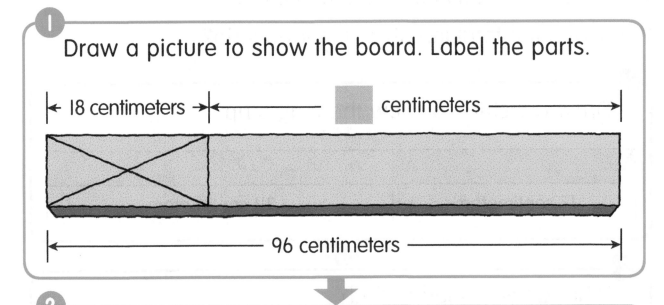

← 18 centimeters →|← ▮ centimeters →

|← 96 centimeters →|

2 Write an equation. You need to find the part of the 96-centimeter board that was left after 18 centimeters was cut off.

$96 - 18 = $ ▮

3 Solve.

$$\begin{array}{r} \overset{8\ 16}{\cancel{9}\ \cancel{6}} \\ -1\ 8 \\ \hline 78 \end{array}$$ ← centimeters of board left

▶ The shelf was _____ centimeters long.

Marni taped two paper strips together end to end.

The orange strip measured 17 centimeters.

The blue strip measured 24 centimeters.

What was the total length of the long strip?

1

Draw a picture to show the long strip.

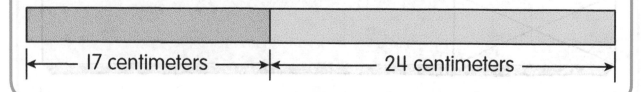

|← 17 centimeters →|← 24 centimeters →|

2

What do you need to find?

total length of the long strip

Write an equation. _____ + _____ =

3

Solve the equation. Show your work.

▶ The total length of the long strip was _____ centimeters.

Practice

Solve. Show your work.

1 LaToya had two pieces of cloth. One piece was 37 inches long. The other was 26 inches long. LaToya joined the pieces to form a banner. What was the total length of the banner?

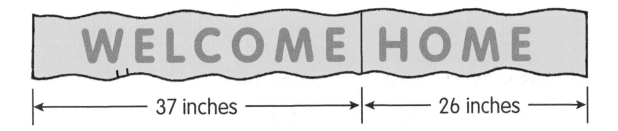

The total length of the banner was _____ inches.

2 A bush was 42 inches long. Adam cut 8 inches off one end. How many inches long was the bush then?

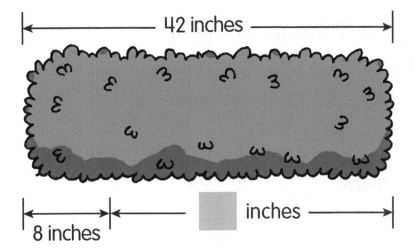

After it was cut, the bush was _____ inches long.

Write and solve an equation. Show your work.

3 Devina has a dotted ribbon that is 47 centimeters long. She has a striped ribbon that is 58 centimeters long. How much longer is the striped ribbon than the dotted ribbon?

Her striped ribbon is _____ centimeters longer.

4 Carlos was 36 inches tall when he started school. Now, in second grade, he is 45 inches tall. How many inches did Carlos grow since he started school?

Carlos grew _____ inches.

5 A tree grew 13 inches last year. It grew 17 inches this year. How many inches did the tree grow over the two years?

The tree grew _____ inches.

6 **SHOW** Jamie's roller skate is 24 centimeters long. Larry's skateboard is 78 centimeters long.

How many centimeters shorter is Jamie's skate than Larry's skateboard? Show your work.

Jamie's skate is _____ centimeters shorter.

Suppose you line up Jamie's two roller skates back to back. Would the total length be longer or shorter than Larry's skateboard? How much longer or shorter?

The total length of the two skates would be

_____ centimeters _____ than the skateboard.

Lesson 22 Number Lines

★ Ordered numbers can be written in a row to form a **number line**. The spaces between the numbers on a number line are equal.

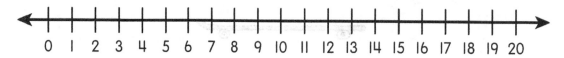

You can use a number line to add.

Example 1

$6 + 12 = $ ▮

1 Use a number line. Start with the greater number. Start at 12.

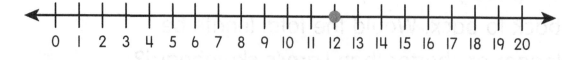

2 Make 6 forward jumps to add 6.

6 jumps end at ___18___.

▶ $6 + 12 = $ ☐

★ You can use a number line to subtract.

Example 2

$19 - 5 = $ ▩

① Use a number line.
Start at 19.

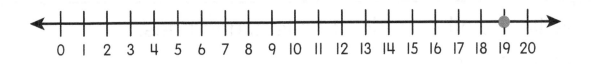

② To subtract 5, take 5 jumps to the left.

5 jumps end at ____14____.

▶ $19 - 5 = $ ☐

Example 3

$17 + 12 = $ ▢

1

Start at the greater addend, 17.

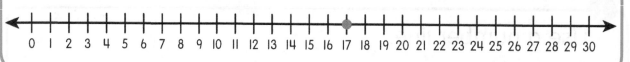

2

Write the other addend as tens and ones.

$12 = 10 + 2$

Add the 10.

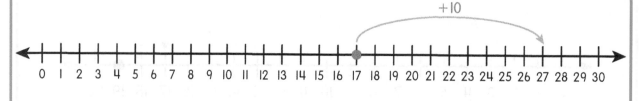

$17 + 10 = 27$

3

Add the 2.

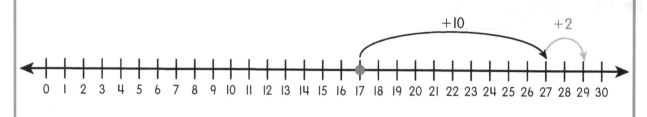

$27 + 2 = \underline{29}$

▶ $17 + 12 = $ ▢

$26 - 14 = $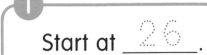

1

Start at __26__.

2

Write 14 as tens and ones.

$14 = 10 + $ _____

Subtract the 10.

$26 - 10 = $ _____

3

Subtract the 4.

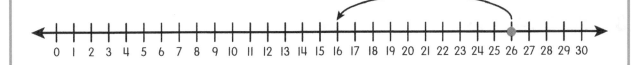

$16 - 4 = $ _____

▶ $26 - 14 = $ _____

Practice

Use the number line.

Show jumps to find the sum or difference.

1   5 + 11 =

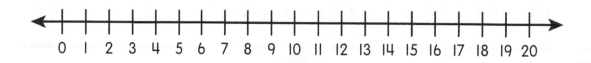

5 + 11 = ☐

....

2   18 − 8 =

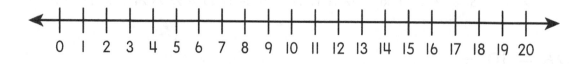

18 − 8 = ☐

....

3   12 + 14 =

12 + 14 = ☐

4 15 + 13 =

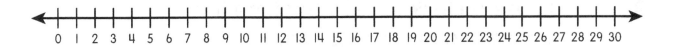

15 + 13 = ☐

5 23 − 14 =

23 − 14 = ☐

6 **DRAW** 19 − 11 =

Complete the number line.
Use it to find the difference.

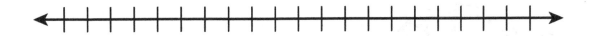

19 − 11 = ☐

★ You can use a **clock** to tell what time it is.
Use **minutes** and **hours** to tell time.

There are 60 minutes in I hour.
There are 30 minutes in I half hour.
There are 15 minutes in I quarter hour.

Each clock below shows 10:15.

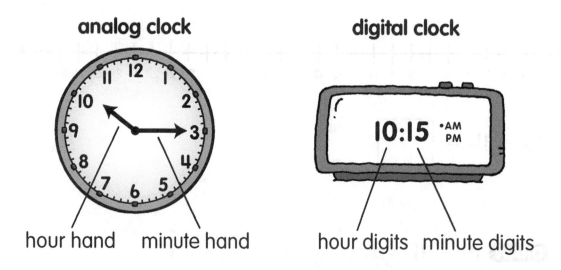

analog clock   digital clock

hour hand   minute hand   hour digits   minute digits

You can skip-count by 5s to read the minutes on a clock.

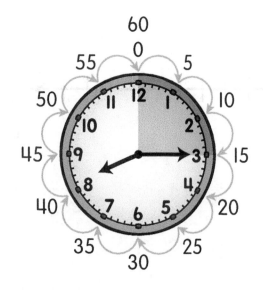

Read the time as:

• 15 minutes past 8 o'clock.

• a quarter after 8.

• eight fifteen.

Example 1

What time does the clock show?

1

Read the hour.

The hour hand is between 3 and 4.

It is past 3 o'clock.

2

Read the minutes.

Start at 12.

Skip-count by 5s.

It is 25 minutes
after 3, or 3:25.

3

Write the time. 3:25

Read 3:25 as twenty-five minutes after three.

▶ The clock shows _____.

★ Use A.M. for any time from 12 midnight to just before 12 noon.

Use P.M. for any time from 12 noon to just before 12 midnight.

Jorge is asleep at 12:00 A.M.

Laura gets to school at 8:05 A.M.

Sumi eats lunch at 12:00 P.M.

Dan gets home from school at 4:15 P.M.

Example 2

The clock shows the time when Sheldon walks his dog each evening. What time does Sheldon walk his dog? Write A.M. or P.M.

1

The hour hand is between 6 and 7.

It is past 6 o'clock.

2

The minute hand points to the 8.

When the minute hand points to the 6, it is 30 minutes past the hour.

Start at the 6. Skip-count by 5s from 30.

It is 40 minutes past 6 o'clock.

3

Write A.M. or P.M.

Evening is P.M., so the time is _6:40 P.M._

▶ Sheldon walks his dog at _____.

The clock shows the time when the children start their math lesson.

What time does the clock show? Write A.M. or P.M.

1

The hour hand is between __10__ and _____.

It is past _____ o'clock.

2

The minute hand points to the _____.

Start at 12 and skip-count by 5s.

It is _____ minutes after _____.

3

10 A.M. is during the day. It is before noon.

10 P.M. is at night.

School is during the day, so the math lesson starts before noon.

Write _____ after the time.

▶ The children start their math lesson at _____.

Write the time shown on the clock.

1

$\underline{1{:}00}$

2

$\underline{2{:}35}$

3

$\underline{2{:}50}$

Draw hands on each clock to show the time.

4 9:20

5 5:30

Write the time shown on the clock. Then write A.M. or P.M.

6

$\underline{11{:}10}$

7

$\underline{3{:}35}$

Which clock shows thirty-five minutes past seven o'clock in the morning?

9 Which clock shows a quarter after two in the afternoon?

10 **SOLVE** The clock shows the time Millie's piano lesson started. How many minutes before four o'clock did her lesson start?

_____ minutes before 4 o'clock

How did you find the answer?

Talk about it.

Lesson 24 Money

★ An amount of money is made up of cents or dollars or both. Use ¢ for cents. Use $ for dollars.

Example 1

José has these coins. How many cents does José have?

1

A **nickel** is worth 5 cents. You can skip-count by 5s to find how many cents three nickels are worth.

5¢   **10¢**   **15¢**

2

A **penny** is worth I cent. Count on from 15 to find how many cents José has.

5¢   10¢   15¢   **16¢**   _17_ ¢

▶ José has _____ cents.

Example 2

Josh has 1 quarter, 2 dimes, and 3 nickels.

How many cents does Josh have?

1

A **quarter** is worth 25 cents.
A **dime** is worth 10 cents.
Start at 25 for the quarter.
Skip-count by 10s for the dimes.

25¢   **35¢**   **45¢**

2

A nickel is worth 5 cents. Start at 45 and skip-count by 5s for the nickels.

25¢   35¢   45¢   **50¢**   **55¢**   _60_

▶ Josh has __60__ cents.

Example 3

Ginny has $17 saved. Her father gives her $8 more.

How many dollars does Ginny have now?

$17 + $8 = __$25__

▶ Now Ginny has _____.

Vicky has 2 quarters, 3 dimes, 2 nickels, and a penny.
How much money does Vicky have?

1

Find the amount for the quarters.
A quarter is 25 cents.

$$
\begin{array}{r}
1 \\
25¢ \\
+25¢ \\
\hline
50¢
\end{array}
$$

2

Start at 50¢. Skip-count by 10s for the 3 dimes.

50¢, __60__, __70__, __80__

3

Start at __80__. Skip-count by 5s for the 2 nickels.

__80__, __85__, __90__

4

Add the penny.
Find how much money Vicky has.

90¢ + __1__ = __91¢__

▶ Vicky has __91¢__.

Find the amount of money. Write ¢ or $.

1 Sofia's coin purse has a quarter, 4 dimes, and 3 pennies in it. How much money does Sofia have in her coin purse?

_68¢_

2 Andrew saved 2 quarters and 7 nickels. How much money has Andrew saved?

_85¢_

3 Cindy found $14 in one drawer of her desk. Then she found $13 in another drawer. How much money did Cindy find in her desk in all?

$ _27.00_

$$14 \\ +13 \\ \overline{27}$$

4 Sean used 3 quarters, a dime, and 2 nickels to pay for an action figure. How much money did Sean spend on the action figure?

_95¢_

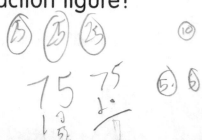

5 Suki put 3 quarters, a dime, and 2 nickels in her coat pocket. On her way home, I dime and I nickel dropped out. How much money did Suki have left in her pocket?

___68___ ¢

---

6 Patrick has $25 to spend on a new toy train engine. If he buys an engine for $18, how much money will he have left?

___$7.00___

7 SHOW Sid puts I quarter, 3 dimes, and 5 nickels into an empty jar. Sally puts I dime, I nickel, and 3 pennies into the same jar. How much money is in the jar now?

Show your work.

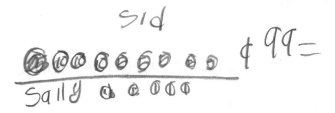

There is __99¢__ in the jar now.

How did you find the answer?

Talk about it.

★ A **line plot** is a way to show **data**.
  The **X**s above a number line show the data.

This is a line plot. It shows the heights of some bushes.

Number of Bushes Measured

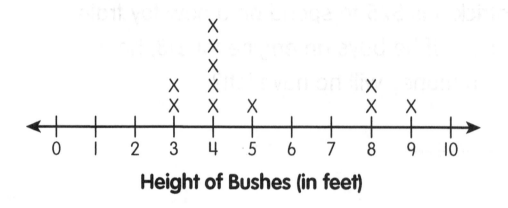

Height of Bushes (in feet)

Each **X** on this line plot stands for one bush.
Each number stands for the height of a bush.

There are no **X**s above the number 1. So no bushes are
1 foot tall.

There are two **X**s above the number 3. So two bushes
are 3 feet tall.

The most **X**s are above the number 4. So the height
that was measured most often is 4 feet.

There are 11 **X**s, so 11 bushes were measured in all.

Example 1

Bob went fishing. He measured the length of each fish he caught. These are his fish-length data.

5 inches	9 inches
10 inches	6 inches
8 inches	10 inches
9 inches	9 inches

Make a line plot of Bob's data.

1

> Draw a number line.
>
> Give the line plot a title.

2

> Use Bob's data.
>
> Draw one **X** for each fish.

▶ **Number of Fish Measured**

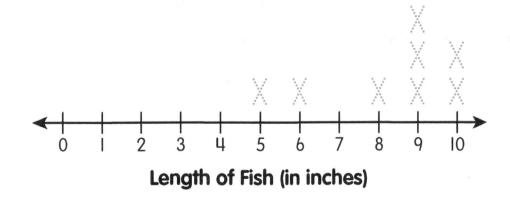

Length of Fish (in inches)

Example 2

Jerry measured the length of these straws
to the nearest centimeter.

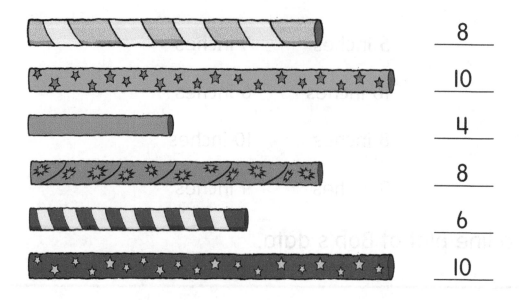

	8
	10
	4
	8
	6
	10

Make a line plot to show Jerry's data.
Draw one X for the length of each straw.

▶ **Number of Straws Measured**

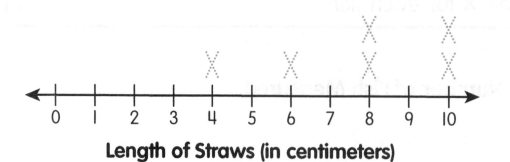

Length of Straws (in centimeters)

Try

Measure the length of each ribbon to the nearest inch.

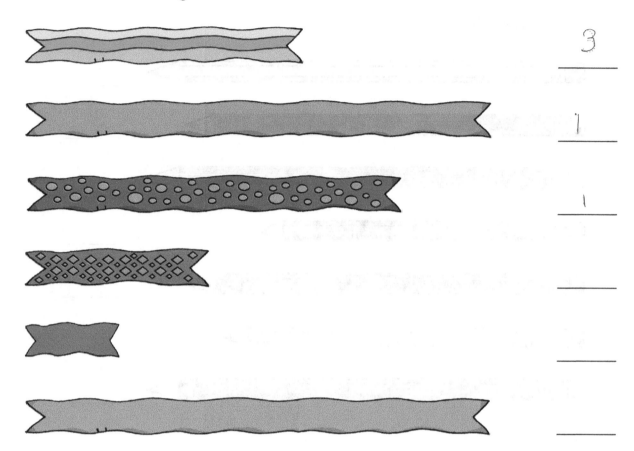

3
_____

1
_____

1
_____

_____

_____

_____

Make a line plot to show your measurement data.
Draw one X for the length of each ribbon.

▶ **Number of Ribbons Measured**

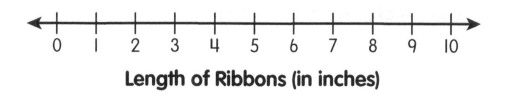

ure the length of each pencil to the
nearest centimeter.

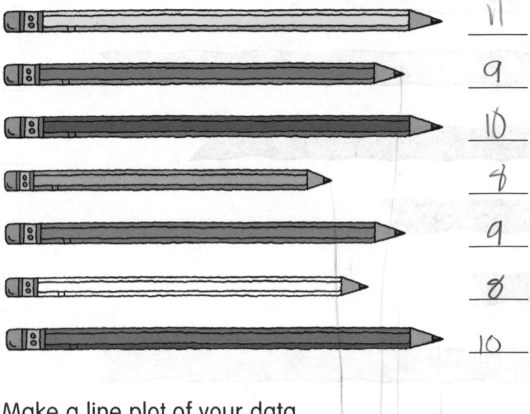

11

9

10

8

9

8

10

Make a line plot of your data.

Number of Pencils Measured

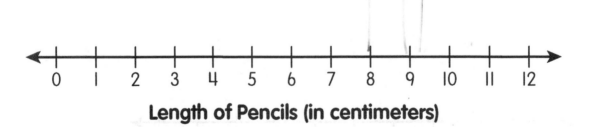

Length of Pencils (in centimeters)

2 **DECIDE** Parks Department workers measured the height of the trees at Highland Park. These are the data they collected.

10 meters	9 meters	4 meters
9 meters	6 meters	8 meters
10 meters	4 meters	10 meters
8 meters	10 meters	9 meters

One worker made this line plot of the data.

Number of Trees Measured

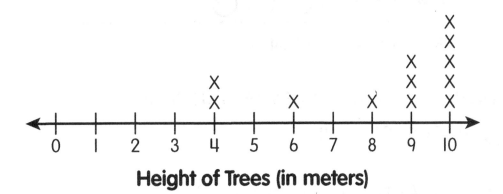

Height of Trees (in meters)

Does the line plot show the data correctly?

_____

Why or why not?

Talk about it.

★ A **picture graph** uses pictures to show data.
The **key** tells what each symbol stands for.

Kate asked her friends to name their favorite fruit. She
made a picture graph of the data she collected.

Favorite Fruit

Apple	◯ ◯ ◯ ◯
Banana	◯ ◯ ◯ ◯ ◯ ◯
Peach	◯ ◯
Strawberry	◯ ◯ ◯

Key: Each ◯ = 1 fruit

In this picture graph, the key tells us that
each ◯ stands for 1 fruit.

In the row for Apple, there are 4 ◯.
So 4 children chose apples as their favorite fruit.

The row for Banana has the most ◯.
So the fruit that was chosen most is bananas.

There are 15 ◯ in the picture graph.
So Kate collected data from 15 friends.

Example 1

Darrell asked his friends how many books they read this month. He made a picture graph of the data he collected.

Books Read

Adam	🕮 🕮 🕮 🕮 🕮
Carla	🕮 🕮 🕮 🕮 🕮 🕮
Julie	🕮 🕮 🕮 🕮
Chung	🕮 🕮 🕮 🕮 🕮

Key: Each 🕮 = 1 book

Which friend read the most books?
How many books did that friend read?

1

Find the row with the most 🕮.

The row for Carla has the most 🕮.

2

Read the key.

Each 🕮 stands for one book.

3

Count the number of 🕮 in the row for Carla.

There are ___6___ 🕮 in the row for Carla.

▶ _____ read the most books. She read _____ books.

Example 2

Mai asked her classmates to name their favorite subject. These are the data she collected.

Reading	5 classmates
Science	6 classmates
Math	5 classmates
Art	8 classmates

Make a picture graph of Mai's data.

1 Choose a symbol for the key.

Let ▲ stand for 1 classmate.

2 Draw the graph.

Give the graph a title.

▶ **Title:** _Favorite Subject_

Reading	▲ ▲ ▲ ▲ ▲
Science	▲ ▲ ▲ ▲ ▲ ▲
Math	▲ ▲ ▲ ▲ ▲
Art	

Key: Each ▲ = 1 classmate

Andres asked his classmates to name their favorite color. Here are the data he collected.

Red	6 classmates
Yellow	5 classmates
Green	6 classmates
Blue	7 classmates

Make a picture graph of Andres's data.

Choose a symbol for the key.

Let △ stand for I classmate.

Draw one △ for each classmate.

Give your graph a title.

▶ **Title:** _____

Red	△ △ △ △ △ △
Yellow	
Green	
Blue	

Key: Each ____ = I classmate

Use the picture graph to answer questions 1–3.

The children in Ms. Lee's class put on a play. The picture graph shows how many tickets they sold.

Tickets Sold

Monday	🎫 🎫 🎫 🎫 🎫 🎫 🎫
Tuesday	🎫 🎫 🎫 🎫 🎫 🎫
Wednesday	🎫 🎫 🎫 🎫
Thursday	🎫 🎫 🎫 🎫 🎫 🎫

Key: Each 🎫 = 1 ticket

1 On which day were the most tickets sold? _Monday_

How many tickets were sold that day? ____7____

2 On which day were the fewest tickets sold? _Wedesday_

How many tickets were sold that day? ____4____

3 How many tickets were sold in all? ____23____

4 **CONSTRUCT** Ella asked her classmates to name their favorite sport. Here are the data she collected.

football	baseball	soccer	basketball
basketball	football	baseball	football
football	soccer	football	soccer
soccer	football	basketball	football

Find the total for each sport.

Football	_____ classmates
Baseball	_____ classmates
Soccer	_____ classmates
Basketball	_____ classmates

Make a picture graph of the data.
Let ◯ stand for 1 classmate. Give your graph a title.

Title: _____

Football	
Baseball	
Soccer	
Basketball	

Key: Each ____ = 1 classmate

⭐ A **bar graph** uses bars to show data.

This bar graph shows the pets of the children in one class.

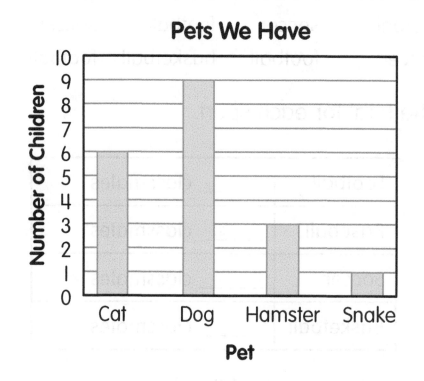

Read the names of the pets along the bottom of the graph.

The tallest bar is for Dog.

So the pet that the most children have is a dog.

The shortest bar is for Snake.

So the pet that the fewest children have is a snake.

Read the numbers along the side of the graph.

The top of the bar for Cat lines up with 6.

So 6 children have a cat.

Example 1

This bar graph shows how some children get to school.

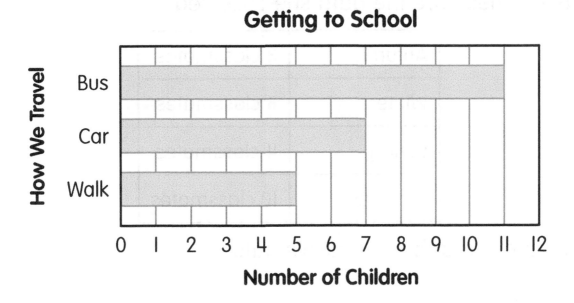

Getting to School

How many more children take the bus than travel by car?

1 Find how many children take the bus.

11 children take the bus.

2 Find how many children travel by car.

7 children travel by car.

3 Subtract to find the difference.

11 − 7 = _____

▶ To get to school, _____ more children take the bus than travel by car.

Example 2

Carissa asked her classmates to name their favorite season. These are the data she collected.

Autumn	3 classmates
Winter	8 classmates
Spring	4 classmates
Summer	10 classmates

Make a bar graph of Carissa's data.

Draw a bar graph.

Give the graph a title.

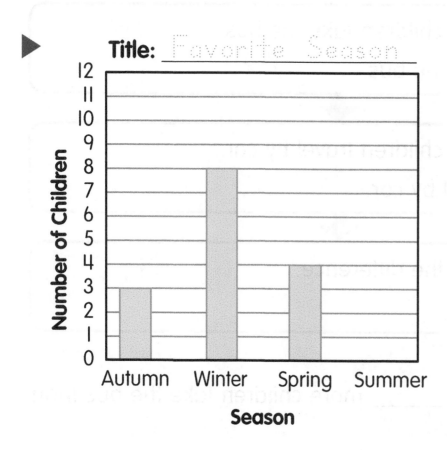

Dylan asked his classmates what they did over the weekend for fun. These are the data he collected.

Bowling	2 classmates
Bike Riding	7 classmates
Went to Movies	9 classmates
Went to Museum	3 classmates

Make a bar graph of Dylan's data.

Draw a bar graph.

Give the graph a title.

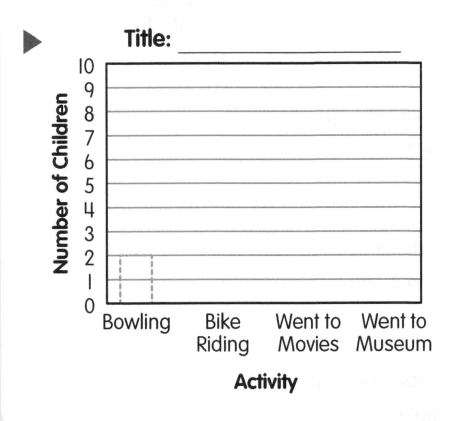

Use the bar graph to answer questions 1–3.

The children in Mr. Johnson's class kept a record of the birds that came to the bird feeder in the school garden. They made this bar graph of the data they collected.

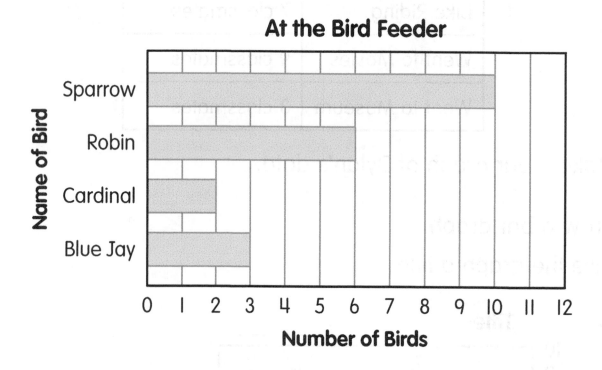

At the Bird Feeder

Name of Bird:
- Sparrow
- Robin
- Cardinal
- Blue Jay

Number of Birds: 0 1 2 3 4 5 6 7 8 9 10 11 12

1 How many robins did the children see at the bird feeder? _____

2 How many cardinals and blue jays did the children see in all? _____

3 How many more sparrows than robins did the children see? _____

4 CONSTRUCT Ms. Garcia listed the kinds of sandwiches the children ate for lunch. Here are the data she collected.

Turkey	7 children
Peanut Butter	8 children
Ham	5 children
Cheese	4 children

Make a bar graph of the data.

Give your graph a title.

Label the sides of your graph.

Title: ______________________

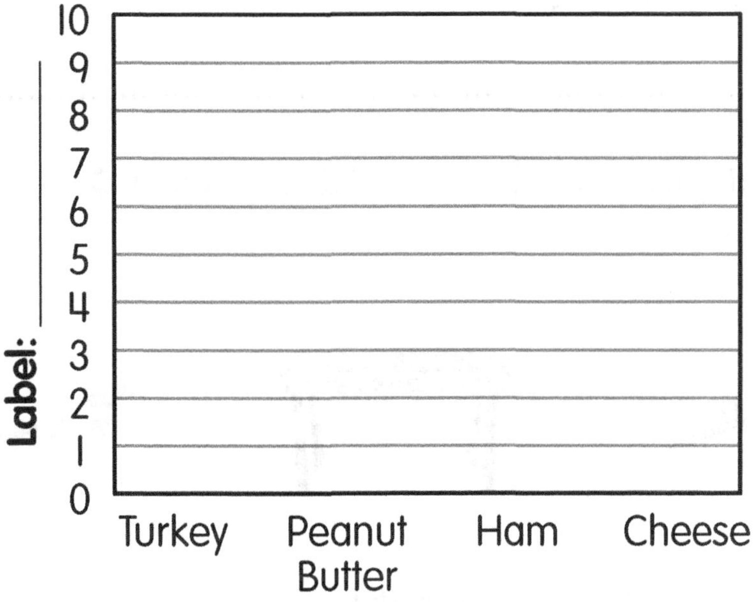

Label: ______________

1 Use an inch ruler to measure the pencil.

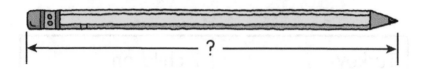

_____ inches

2 Use a centimeter ruler to measure the crayon.

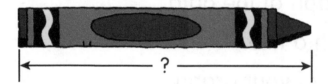

_____ centimeters

3 Which length would you measure with a yardstick?

a pencil   a table   a key

4 Use an inch ruler to measure the length of this flower.

Then use a centimeter ruler to measure the flower.

_____ inches   _____ centimeters

Does it take more inches or more centimeters to measure the length of the flower?

It takes more _____.

5 Estimate the length of the feather.

Then use an inch ruler to measure it.

estimate: _____ inches

measurement: _____ inches

6 Use a centimeter ruler to measure each piece of yarn.

How much longer than the pink yarn is the green yarn?

_____ centimeters

_____ centimeters

The green yarn is _____ centimeters longer than the pink yarn.

··

Write and solve an equation. Show your work.

7 Isla's toy box was 28 inches high. She put another box on it that is 14 inches high.

What is the total height of the toy box now?

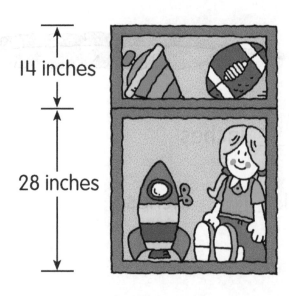

14 inches

28 inches

The total height of the toy box is _____ inches.

8 Tobin ran 76 meters today. Yesterday he ran 59 meters. How much farther did Tobin run today than yesterday?

Tobin ran _____ meters farther today.

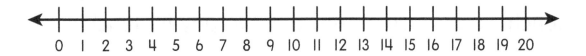

Use the number line.
Show jumps to find the sum or difference.

9 4 + 13 = ▢

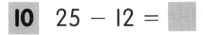

4 + 13 = ▢

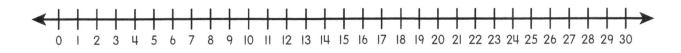

10 25 − 12 = ▢

25 − 12 = ▢

Write the time shown on the clock. Then write A.M. or P.M.

11

12

_____   _____

....

Find the amount of money. Write ¢ or $.

13 Ava used 2 quarters, I dime, and I nickel to pay for lunch. How much money did Ava pay for lunch?

_____

....

14 Jarell spent $22 on a gift for his sister. He spent another $15 on a toy for himself. How much money did Jarell spend?

_____

15 Measure the length of each line to the nearest centimeter.

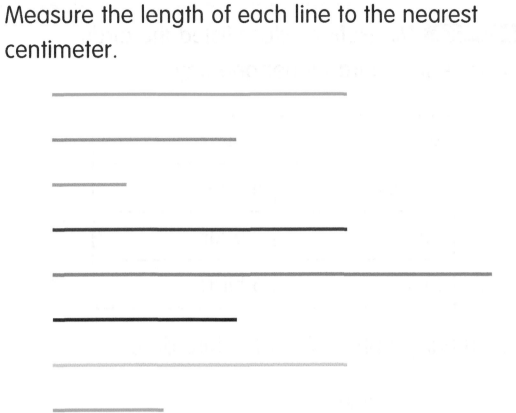

Make a line plot of your data.

Number of Lines Measured

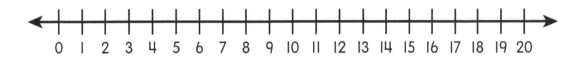

Length of Lines (in centimeters)

16 CONSTRUCT Mr. Hoffer's class listed the birds that came to its bird feeder one day.

Sparrow	5 birds
Nuthatch	4 birds
Finch	9 birds
Junco	6 birds

Make a bar graph to show the bird data.

Title: _____

10	
9	
8	
7	
6	
5	
4	
3	
2	
1	
0	Sparrow Nuthatch Finch Junco

Label: _____

Label: _____

Juan asked four friends how many dollar bills they each had.

The picture graph shows some of his data.

Use the clues to draw dollar bills for Zac and Amber.

Clue 1 No one has as many dollar bills as Nori.

Clue 2 Amber has more dollar bills than Chane.

Clue 3 Zac has 2 fewer dollar bills than Amber.

Number of Dollar Bills

Nori	🟦 🟦 🟦 🟦 🟦 🟦
Zac	
Amber	
Chane	🟦 🟦 🟦 🟦

Key: Each 🟦 = $1

How much money do the four children have in all?

Show your work.

Talk about it.

The four children have _____ in all.

How did you find your answer?

Domain 4
Geometry

Domain 4
Geometry

How can you show two halves of the plain pizza?

★ Here are some flat shapes with straight **sides** and **angles**.

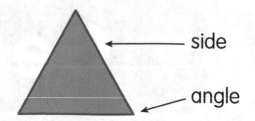

side

angle

Shape	Example	Number of Straight Sides	Number of Angles
triangle		3	3
square		4	4
rectangle		4	4
trapezoid		4	4
pentagon		5	5
hexagon		6	6

Squares, rectangles, and trapezoids are **quadrilaterals**.
A quadrilateral is a flat shape with 4 straight sides
and 4 angles.

A **circle** is a curved flat shape. It has
no straight sides and no angles.

Example 1

Which banner has the shape of a quadrilateral?

1

Count the number of sides and angles of each banner.

The green banner has 6 sides and 6 angles.

The orange banner has 4 sides and 4 angles.

2

Think about what you know about a quadrilateral.

It is a flat shape with 4 straight sides and 4 angles.

So the ___orange___ banner has the shape of a quadrilateral.

The ___green___ banner has the shape of a hexagon.

▶ The _____ banner has the shape of a quadrilateral.

★ You can use dot paper to draw shapes.

Example 2

Draw a triangle.

1 Think about what a triangle looks like.

A triangle has 3 straight sides and 3 angles.

2 Use dot paper. Draw two straight lines that meet.

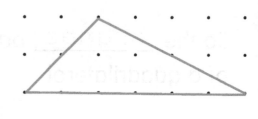

3 Draw a third straight line that connects the first two lines.

▶ Now draw a triangle on the dot paper.

★ Some solid shapes have **faces**.
This shape is a **cube**.
A cube has 6 faces.

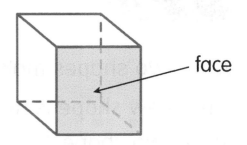
face

Example 3

What shape is each face of a cube?

1   Look at the blue face.

There are 4 sides and 4 angles.

All the sides are the same length.

All the angles are the same shape.

So the shape of the blue face is a square.

2   Look at the other faces of the cube.

All the faces are the same size and shape.

So each face of a cube has the shape

of a ___square___.

▶ Each face of a cube has the shape of a _____.

What two shapes make up this picture?

What new shape is made from
these two shapes?

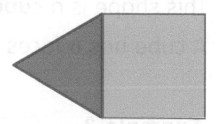

1

Look at the red shape.

It has __3__ straight sides and __3__ angles.

The red shape is a _____.

2

Look at the green shape.

It has _____ straight sides and _____ angles.

Are all sides the same length? _____

Are all angles the same shape? _____

The green shape is a _____.

3

Look at the new shape.

It has _____ straight sides and _____ angles.

▶ The new shape is a _____.

Write how many sides and angles. Name the shape.

1

_____ sides

_____ angles

_____

2

_____ sides

_____ angles

_____

Write the name of the shape.

3

_____

4

_____

5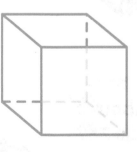

_____

6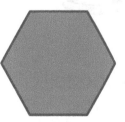

_____

7 Which is not a pentagon?

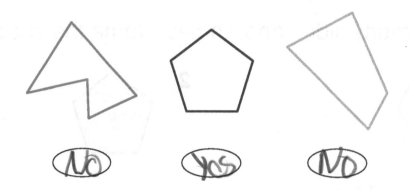

No   Yes   No

8 Which is not a quadrilateral?

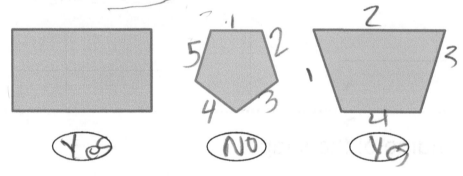

Yes   No   Yes

9 (EXPLAIN) Which object has the shape of a cube?

How can you tell?

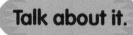

Talk about it.

Making Same-Size Squares in Rectangles

This rectangle is made up of 6 same-size squares.
There are 2 rows of squares.
There are 3 columns of squares.

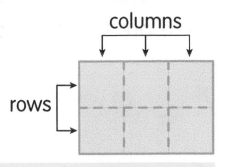

Example 1

How many rows and columns make up this rectangle?

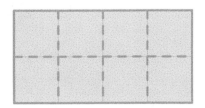

1 How many rows of same-size squares?

There are 2 rows of same-size squares.

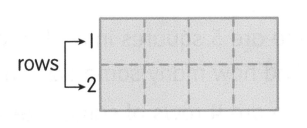

2 How many columns of same-size squares?

There are _____ columns of same-size squares.

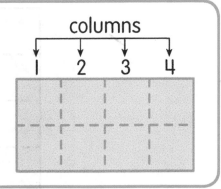

▶ There are _____ rows and _____ columns of same-size squares in the rectangle.

Example 2

This rectangle is made up of same-size squares.
There are 4 rows and 5 columns of same-size squares.

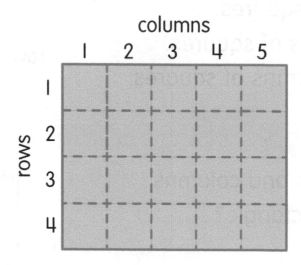

How many same-size squares are in the rectangle?

There are 5 squares in each row. Skip-count by 5s
to find how many same-size squares.

There are 4 rows of same-size squares.
Skip-count by 5s four times.

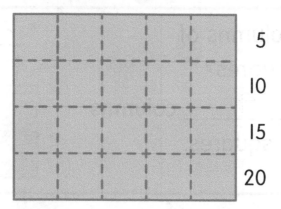

5, 10, 15, __20__

▶ There are _____ same-size squares in the rectangle.

Example 3

How many same-size squares are in this rectangle?

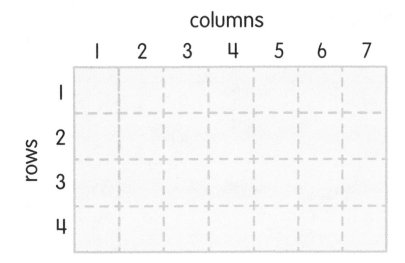

1 Find the number of same-size squares in each row.
There are 7 squares in each row.

2 Count the number of rows. There are 4 rows.
Each row has 7 same-size squares.

3 Add the four 7s: $7 + 7 + 7 + 7 =$ ▪

$7 + 7 = 14$

$14 + 7 = 21$

$21 + 7 = \boxed{28}$

▶ There are _____ same-size squares in the rectangle.

 **Try**

How many same-size squares are in this rectangle?

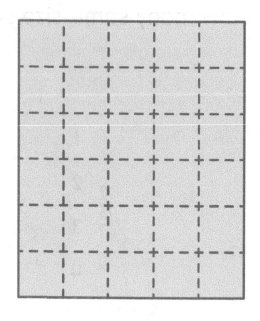

1 Count the rows.

The rectangle has _6_ rows.

2 Count the number of squares in each row.

There are _____ squares in each row.

3 You can skip-count by _____ six times.

_____, _____, _____, _____, _____, _____

▶ There are _____ same-size squares in the rectangle.

Write how many rows and columns.

1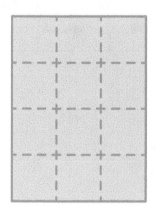

_____ rows

_____ columns

2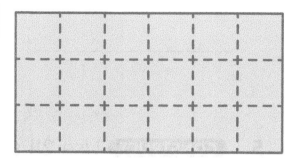

_____ rows

_____ columns

3 Draw a rectangle on the grid. Write how many rows and columns your rectangle has. Write how many same-size squares make up your rectangle.

_____ rows

_____ columns

_____ same-size squares

4 How many same-size squares are in this rectangle?

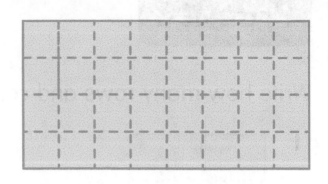

_____

5 CONSTRUCT Use 24 same-size squares to make a rectangle.

How many rows of squares are in your rectangle?

_____ rows

How many squares are in each row? _____

Do you think you could have made a different rectangle with 24 squares?

Talk about it.

Lesson 30 Making Equal Shares

★ You can break up a whole shape into **equal shares.**

This square has 2 equal shares.

Each is a **half of** the whole square.

The whole square is equal to 2 **halves**.

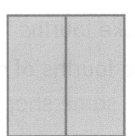

This circle has 4 equal shares.

Each is a **fourth of** the whole circle.

The whole circle is equal to 4 **fourths**.

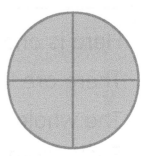

Example I

What share of this circle is blue?

Count the equal shares. There are 3 equal shares.

The whole circle is equal to 3 **thirds**.

Each share is a **third of** the whole.

So the blue share is a ___third___ of the whole circle.

▶ The blue share is a _____ of the circle.

★ There is more than one way to break up a shape into equal shares.

Example 2

Use this rectangle.

Make fourths in different ways.

Are fourths of a rectangle always the same shape?

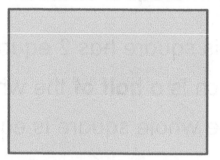

①
Here is one way to make fourths.

There are 4 equal shares.

The whole is 4 fourths.
Each share is a fourth.

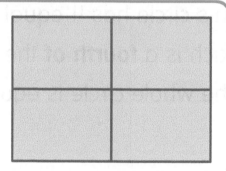

②
Here is another way to make fourths.

There are 4 equal shares.

The whole is 4 ___fourths___.

Each share is a ___fourth___.

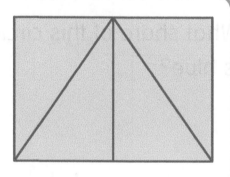

▶ Are fourths of a rectangle always the same shape?

_____

 Try

Two whole squares are shown below.
The squares are the same size.

Sarah divided the red square into equal shares.

Chuck divided the blue square into equal shares.

What can we say about Sarah's and Chuck's equal shares?

How many equal shares did Sarah make? ___4___

How many equal shares did Chuck make? _____

Are the equal shares the same shape? _____

▶ Each share is a _____ of the square.

The equal shares do not have the same _____.

Write halves, thirds, or fourths.

1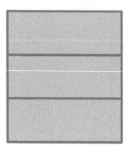

_____

2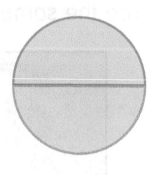

_____

3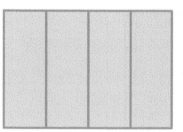

_____

4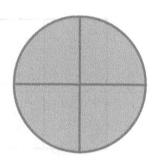

_____

Write half, third, or fourth to make the sentence true.

5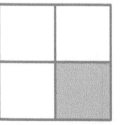

A _____
of the shape is red.

6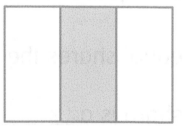

A _____
of the shape is blue.

7 **DRAW** Break up this rectangle into halves.
Color a half of the rectangle red.

How many equal shares did you make? _____

How many halves are in 1 whole? _____

Break up the rectangle into halves another way.
Color a half of the rectangle red.

How many equal shares did you make? _____

Look at the equal shares in both rectangles.
Are the equal shares the same shape?

Are the equal shares the same size?

How do you know?

Talk about it.

Write how many sides and angles. Name the shape.

1

_____ sides

_____ angles

_____

2

_____ sides

_____ angles

_____

3 What is the name of the shape?

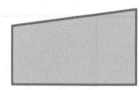

a square   a rectangle   a quadrilateral

4 Which is a cube?

   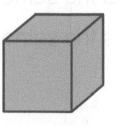   

5 Draw a flat shape with 6 straight sides and 6 angles.

The shape I drew is a _____.

....

6 Draw a rectangle on the grid. Write how many rows and columns your rectangle has. Write how many same-size squares make up your rectangle.

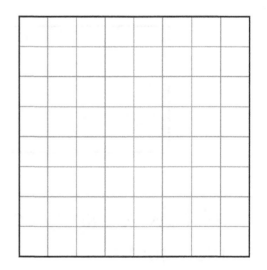

_____ rows

_____ columns

_____ same-size squares

Write halves, thirds, or fourths.

7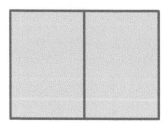

_____

8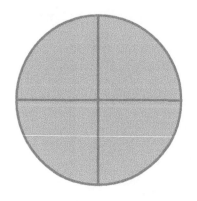

_____

9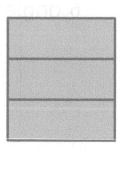

_____

10 DRAW The two whole rectangles below are the same size. Show two different ways to break up the rectangles into equal shares.

Tell how you know each rectangle is broken into equal shares.

Talk about it.

MAKE A BANNER

Your class is having a banner contest.

Each student will make a banner from squares.

Use a square like this.

Make your banner

Step 1 Put together 2, 3, or 4 squares in a row.

Step 2 Color each square a different color.

1 What shape is your banner? _____

2 How many squares did you use? _____

3 How many equal shares is your whole banner divided into? _____

4 Is each share a half, a third, or a fourth of your whole banner?

How do you know?

Talk about it.

Glossary

A

add to find how many in all (Lesson 1)

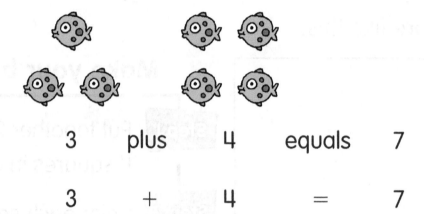

| 3 | plus | 4 | equals | 7 |

| 3 | + | 4 | = | 7 |

addends the numbers you add (Lesson 1)

$$3 + 2 = 5$$
$$\uparrow \quad \uparrow$$
addends

angle a corner of a flat shape (Lesson 28)

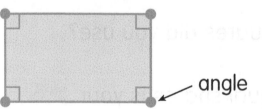

angle

array a group that has the same number of objects in each row (Lesson 5)

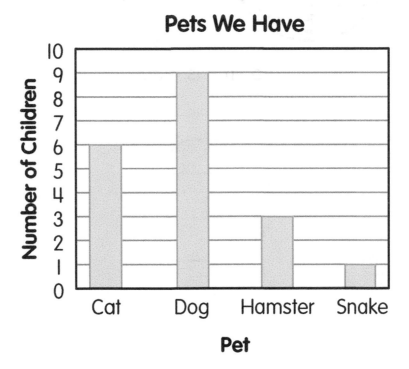

 B

bar graph a graph that uses bars to show data (Lesson 27)

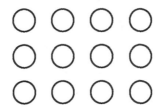

C

centimeter a unit of length used to measure small objects (Lesson 17)

A crayon is 10 centimeters long.

circle a flat shape with a curved side and 0 angles (Lesson 28)

clock (Lesson 23)

The time is 4:30.

cube (Lesson 28)

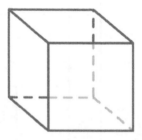

data information (Lesson 25)

difference the answer in subtraction (Lesson 2)

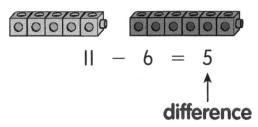

$$11 - 6 = 5$$

↑
difference

digit (Lesson 8)

The number 362 has 3 digits.

dime a coin worth 10 cents or 10¢ (Lesson 24)

dollar a bill worth 1 dollar or $1 (Lesson 24)

equal shares (Lesson 30)

This rectangle is in 4 equal shares.

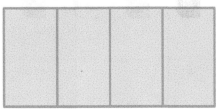

equal to (=) (Lesson 9)

$$22 = 22$$
↑
is equal to

equation a number sentence with an equal sign (Lesson 1)

$$4 + 6 = 10$$

$$9 - 2 = 7$$

$$5 + 3 = 3 + 5$$

estimate close to the exact amount (Lesson 19)

A pencil is about 6 inches long. 6 inches is an estimate.

even numbers (Lesson 4)

You can make pairs with even numbers.

8 is an even number.

expanded form a way to write a number (Lesson 8)

100 + 30 + 7 is the expanded form for 137.

face a flat side of a solid shape (Lesson 28)

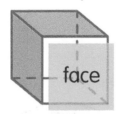

face

foot a unit used to measure lengths of large objects (Lesson 16)

A car is 12 feet long.

fourths (Lesson 30)

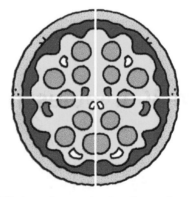

This pizza is in fourths.

greater than (>) (Lesson 9)

22 > 16
↑
is greater than

half (halves) (Lesson 30)

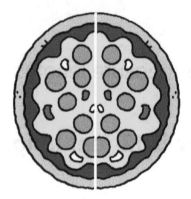

This pizza is in halves.

half hour (Lesson 23)

There are 30 minutes in a half hour.

hexagon (Lesson 28)

hour (Lesson 23)

There are 60 minutes in 1 hour.

inch a unit used to measure lengths of small objects (Lesson 16)

A pencil is 6 inches long.

key the part of a picture graph that shows what each picture means (Lesson 26)

Cakes Sold

Day	Number of Cakes
Friday	🍰 🍰 🍰
Saturday	🍰 🍰 🍰 🍰 🍰 🍰
Sunday	🍰 🍰 🍰 🍰 🍰

Key: Each 🍰 = 1 cake

length how long something is (Lesson 16)

less than (<) (Lesson 9)

$$16 < 22$$
↑
is less than

line plot a graph that uses a number line and Xs to show data (Lesson 25)

Number of Candles Measured

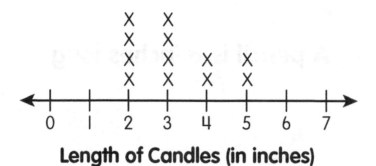

Length of Candles (in inches)

meter a unit used to measure the lengths of large objects (Lesson 17)

A blackboard is 2 meters long.

minute (Lesson 23)

There are 60 minutes in 1 hour.

nickel a coin worth 5 cents or 5¢ (Lesson 24)

number line (Lesson 22)

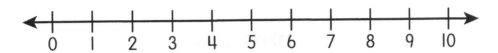

number name a number in words (Lesson 8)

One hundred thirty is the number name for 130.

odd numbers (Lesson 4)

9 is an odd number.

penny a coin worth 1 cent or 1¢ (Lesson 24)

pentagon (Lesson 28)

picture graph a graph that uses pictures to show data (Lesson 26)

Cakes Sold

Day	Number of Cakes
Friday	
Saturday	
Sunday	

Key: Each = I cake

quadrilateral a flat shape with 4 sides and 4 angles (Lesson 28)

These shapes are quadrilaterals.

quarter a coin worth 25 cents or 25¢ (Lesson 24)

quarter hour (Lesson 23)

There are 15 minutes in a quarter hour.

side a straight line on a flat shape (Lesson 28)

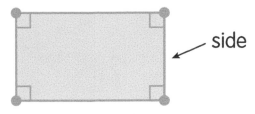

side

skip-count (Lesson 7)

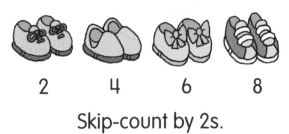

2   4   6   8

Skip-count by 2s.

subtract to find how many are left (Lesson 2)

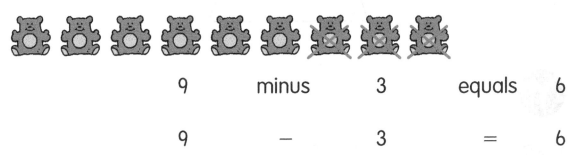

9   minus   3   equals   6

9   –   3   =   6

sum the answer in addition (Lesson 1)

$$6 \quad + \quad 5 \quad = \quad 11$$

sum

third (Lesson 30)

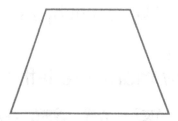

trapezoid (Lesson 28)

yard a unit used to measure lengths of large objects (Lesson 16)

A yard is 3 feet long.
A yard is 36 inches long.

Math Tool: Addend-Addend-Sum Mat

Name _____

Math Tool: Ten Frame

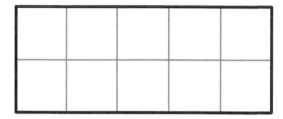

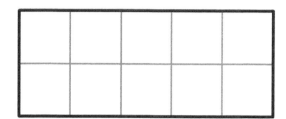

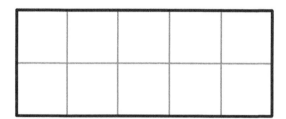

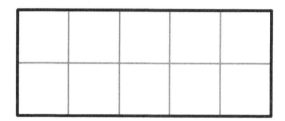

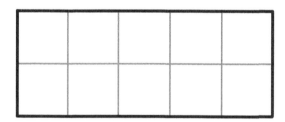

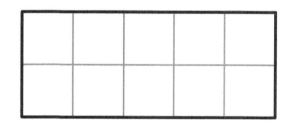

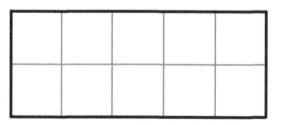

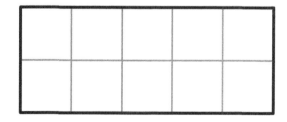

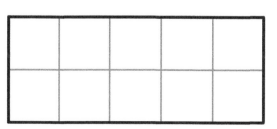

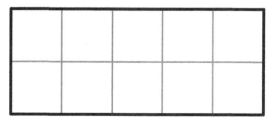

Math Tool: Ten Frame

Math Tool: Hundred Chart

1	2	3	4	5	6	7	8	9	10
11	12	13	14	15	16	17	18	19	20
21	22	23	24	25	26	27	28	29	30
31	32	33	34	35	36	37	38	39	40
41	42	43	44	45	46	47	48	49	50
51	52	53	54	55	56	57	58	59	60
61	62	63	64	65	66	67	68	69	70
71	72	73	74	75	76	77	78	79	80
81	82	83	84	85	86	87	88	89	90
91	92	93	94	95	96	97	98	99	100

Math Tool: Hundreds, Tens, Ones Chart A

Hundreds	Tens	Ones

Hundreds	Tens	Ones

Hundreds	Tens	Ones

Hundreds	Tens	Ones

Hundreds	Tens	Ones

Hundreds	Tens	Ones

Hundreds	Tens	Ones

Hundreds	Tens	Ones

Name _____

Math Tool: Tens and Ones Chart B

Tens	Ones
3	2
+	

Tens	Ones
−	

Tens	Ones
+	

Tens	Ones
−	

Tens	Ones
+	

Tens	Ones
−	

Math Tool: Hundreds, Tens, Ones Chart C

Hundreds	Tens	Ones
+		

Hundreds	Tens	Ones
−		

Hundreds	Tens	Ones
+		

Hundreds	Tens	Ones
−		

Hundreds	Tens	Ones
+		

Hundreds	Tens	Ones
−		

Name _____

Math Tool: Clocks

Math Tool: Clocks

Math Tool: Digital Clocks

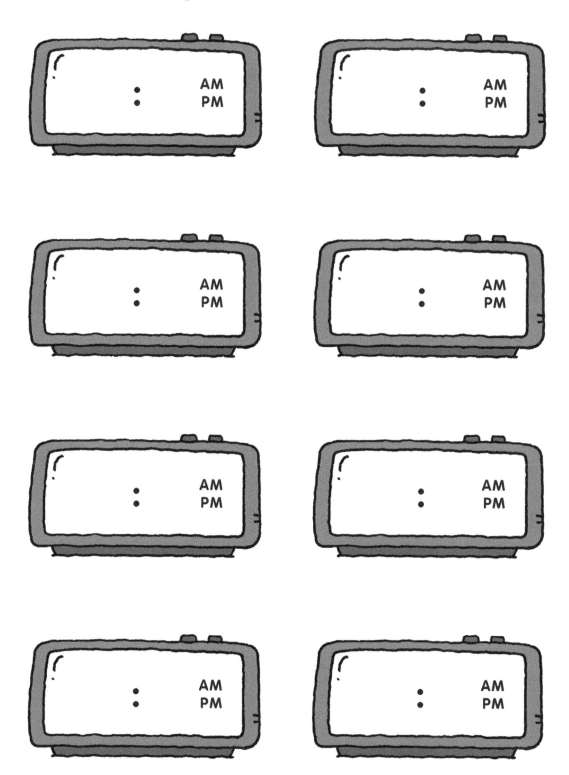

Math Tool: Number Lines

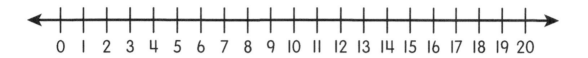

0 1 2 3 4 5 6 7 8 9 10 11 12 13 14 15 16 17 18 19 20

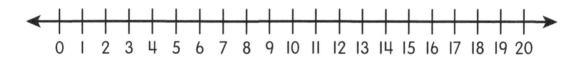

0 1 2 3 4 5 6 7 8 9 10 11 12 13 14 15 16 17 18 19 20

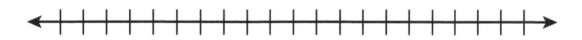

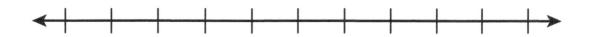

Math Tool: Dot Paper

Math Tool: Grid Paper

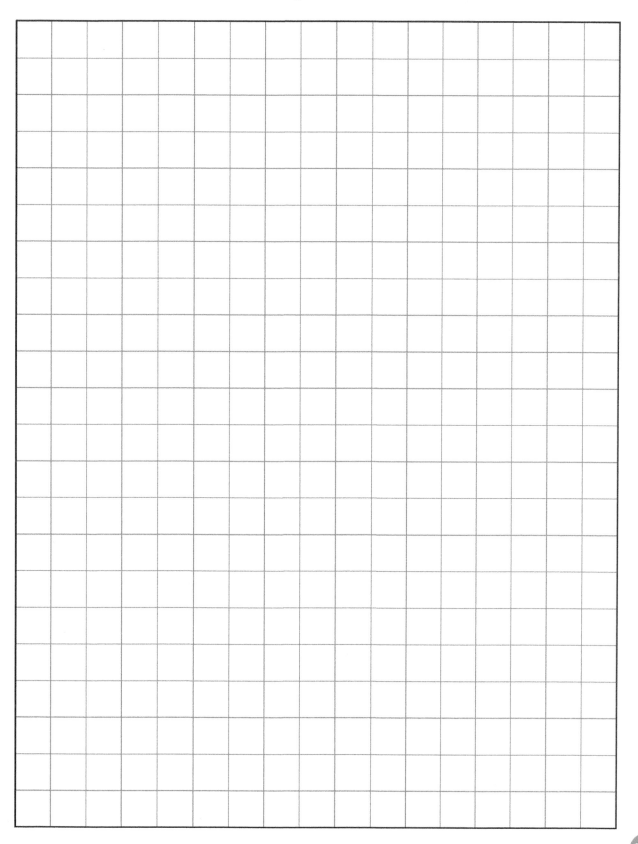